Free Your
Mind
In Just 14 Days

A REVOLUTIONARY MIND TRAINING PROGRAMME
TO OVERCOME GENERAL ANXIETY, CHRONIC WORRY,
SOCIAL ANXIETY AND PANIC ATTACKS

Tim Patch

Published by Tim Patch
www.freethemindtraining.com
Enquiries can be directed by email to:
tim@freethemindtraining.com

Illustrations by Anna Lloyd
Cover Design by Rock Solid Book Design

ISBN 978-1-5272-2564-0

Contents

I dedicate this book to all who bravely battle each day with anxiety and worry. It is my sincerest desire that this book equips you with new strategies to better understand and overcome your anxiety to live a happy, fulfilling life with a blissfully free mind.

"Do not let your difficulties fill you with anxiety, after all it is only in the darkest nights that stars shine more brightly."

Hazrat Ali Ibn Abu-Talib A.S.

Introduction

You open your front door to leave for work but stop. Your stomach churns with foreboding as you sense an impending doom. A dull thought slowly worms its way into the back of your mind, "Today's going to be an awful day." You then find yourself wondering, "Why do I think so negatively? Come on. You can do better than this. But what if?"

Later that morning, you are asked to give a presentation, but your throat constricts as you imagine faltering in front of an impatient audience. Your heart thumps so rapidly you can feel its pulse in your ears. You cannot face giving the presentation, so you turn it down, chiding yourself as you do. "I'm such a failure", you think.

You spend the rest of the afternoon agonising over what your colleagues must think of you. "Do they take me seriously? Do they think I'm incompetent?" You find yourself re-reading the same line in an email over and again, unable to focus, unable to take anything in. "I can't do this," you think. "This is all too much for me."

At the end of an exhausting day, you throw yourself wearily into bed. You have navigated a minefield of negative emotions and now desperately need to sleep. But your ruminating mind babbles noisily, mercilessly replaying sketchy reminders of the day and how things did not go as planned. You spend the early hours of the morning tossing, turning and napping. "I can't do this," you sigh for the hundredth time. "Why can everyone else cope except me?"

Can you relate to any of these scenarios?

Do you worry constantly, have trouble relaxing or sleeping?

Do you feel overwhelmed by your fears?

Have you reached a point in your life where you feel something MUST change for the better – today?

Everyone gets anxious from time to time, perhaps when encountering something unfamiliar, going through financial uncertainty or simply worrying about loved ones. That type of anxiety is normal.

But for some people, anxiety has become so frequent, it has taken over their lives. I remember only too well what it is like to live with a persistent, all-consuming unease, bearing down on me until I wondered if I would ever survive under the strain.

This is chronic anxiety and it has no redeeming features. It leads to restlessness and sleepless nights, robs you of focus or clarity of mind, and has you lacking confidence in your abilities. At best, you feel you are living life below par, at worst as if you are losing your mind.

My earliest memory of anxiety was in my teens as a goalkeeper for my school football team. I would worry for hours before a match.

"What if I let in a goal? What if I mess up? What if I let everyone down?"

While I am sure it is not uncommon for any youngster to worry about letting down their team, my 'what-ifs' overwhelmed me, filling me with dread.

Despite this, I enjoyed sports and as I got older, took up tennis. But this meant more opportunities to become anxious, with nerve-wracking hours before matches fearing failure or panicking about how a match would end.

I went on to university to suffer crippling panic attacks so severe, they often left me mentally and physically drained. My friends saw me as a regular person and would have had no clue what was going on. I turned up at lectures, loved talking about sport and went out in the evening like everyone else. What they did not see was my raging, chattering mind.

There is only so much anyone can bottle up. By the time I left university, I knew I had to find a way to overcome the beast that was robbing me of peace of mind. I wanted to, quite literally, understand what was going on inside my head.

"We cannot be what we need to be by remaining what we are." Max DuPree.

It is no exaggeration to say that in my quest for recovery, I read scores of books. Some loaded with medical jargon I found hard to understand, others a tad superficial and others completely unhelpful. But I persevered, pouring everything I learned into creating a training programme to help me get through the rest of my twenties and ultimately, a successful twenty-year career in the City of London.

I later refined and perfected the programme until it became what it is today. An approach that draws upon neuroscientific research, with the evidence-based benefits of meditation, self-hypnosis, and visualisation. The latter – visualisation – is the real key to success.

This programme not only brings a refreshingly new perspective to the understanding of anxiety and how you can take full advantage of the most up-to-date self-help methodologies out there, it fully equips you with the tools you need to understand and overcome your anxiety for good.

But before I tell you more about the programme, let me share some facts about anxiety:

- The most recent figures indicate that around the globe, 1 in 13 people suffer from an anxiety disorder[1]. According to the World Health Organization (WHO), this equates to an estimated 264 million people[2].

- By the year 2020, anxiety disorders will be the second leading cause of disability worldwide (the first being depression)[3], and because anxiety disorders can mimic depression with symptoms ranging from trouble concentrating, restlessness, irritability, fatigue and difficulty in sleeping, they are often misdiagnosed[4].

- Anxiety disorders lead to a considerable loss in health and functioning, which if left untreated lead to school or work drop-out, relationship breakdown, depression or suicide[5].

- Conventional treatments for anxiety disorders include mild anti-depressants called SSRIs (selective serotonin reuptake inhibitors). This is because serotonin, a chemical 'messenger' that carries signals between brain cells, plays a key role in determining moods. You could think of it as a mood stabiliser. As people with anxiety disorders are believed to have low levels of serotonin, SSRIs are prescribed to allow more serotonin to be released into the brain. However, there are always limitations to the effectiveness of any drug or medication, and in some instances even side effects. Of note are recent guidelines by NICE, which indicates that people who have used medication for anxiety or depression, find self-help techniques with psychological therapies keep them feeling well for longer[6].

The really worrying part? The statistics I have cited above are of people with a diagnosed anxiety disorder. According to Mind mental health charity in the UK, these are: Generalised Anxiety Disorder (GAD); Social Anxiety Disorder; Panic Disorder; Phobias; Post Traumatic Stress Disorder (PSTD); Obsessive Compulsive Disorder (OCD); Body dysmorphic disorder (BDD) and Perinatal anxiety or perinatal OCD.[7]

The statistics I cite above do not include people who have not visited their doctor or health practitioner for a diagnosis. This clearly puts the number of people around the globe who suffer from other forms of anxiety such as chronic worry or panic attacks at much higher than 264 million.

Of more concern, is that anxiety is often misunderstood or swept aside with sweeping generalisations such as, "try not to worry", "I'm sure you'll get over it", or "snap out of it, pull yourself together". Comments like these are of course completely unhelpful and simply remind the person they have something to worry about, making them feel lonely and isolated.

I have called my training programme Free the Mind because a free mind is exactly what you will achieve. But with one caveat. If you fully commit to the programme and carefully apply the techniques I teach in it.

"The life you have led doesn't need to be the only life you have." Anna Quindlen.

With this programme, you will learn how to change your relationship with anxiety. How to understand it, manage it and ultimately overcome it.

Overall, you will learn:

- What anxiety is: its symptoms, pathways, and how an understanding of those pathways are key to your recovery.

- What happens during an anxiety attack: I share neuroscientific research of the brain's activity when anxiety occurs.

- How to refocus and reframe your thoughts: learn why your thoughts may have held you back and how you can reframe them to create powerful, long-lasting change for the better.

- How to apply the mind training techniques: by using the programme for just 15 minutes a day for 14 days, you will notice a remarkable change in the way you react to situations that would normally cause you anxiety. Your mind will be freer to allow you to focus on the job at hand and with practice, overcome your anxiety for good.

When I searched for help to overcome my anxiety thirty years ago, I was not satisfied with soundbites telling me to "have a positive mental attitude" or "don't worry, be happy". Just as there is little point in embellishing a room with niceties if the room is full to the brim with clutter, shallow platitudes are of little value if your 'monkey mind' will not stop chattering ten to the dozen.

I wanted to be rid of the awful feeling in the pit of my stomach and the shackles of anxiety holding me back from living a normal life. I wanted a permanent cure. I am sure you do too.

Physicians have long understood the body's ability to heal itself by using the power of the mind, referred to as the mind-body connection. Take for example, the placebo (a fake medicine or procedure). When trialling the effectiveness of medicine or a procedure, the placebo will be tested in a double-blind study where the placebo is given to a test group and the real drug/treatment to a control group. Neither group will be told who receives what. A record will simply be made whether the real drug/treatment performs significantly better than the placebo. If it does not, it will not be approved.

The placebo has, at times, shown beneficial results – in some instances a complete cure – which obviously cannot be attributed to the 'fake' properties of the placebo. One medical study for example, found that meditation, yoga and support group therapy can alter DNA[8]. If your mind can alter DNA – which contains the genetic 'instructions' for cell development – how powerful does that make your mind? This study is a fascinating one, which I refer to in the chapter "Why Train the Mind?"

But a question arises. How is it possible for the mind to trick the body into healing?

Henry Beecher[9] a pioneering pharmacologist and anaesthesiologist investigated the placebo and its effect on the mind, initially observing how the psychological state of soldiers wounded in the second world war influenced their perception of pain. His studies led him to believe that the placebo worked as effectively as medicine 30-40% of the time.

Beecher's calculations have since been updated, and Bruce Mosely an orthopaedic surgeon, took the study of the placebo even further. In one study, he took 180 patients who were suffering from osteoarthritis of the knee and divided them into three groups: the first had full surgery, the second had rinsing of the knee and the third had placebo surgery.

During the placebo surgery, incisions were made in the joint to give the impression that surgery was being carried out, and saline splashed in it to stimulate the sound of the knee being rinsed. The result of the experiment? During postoperative care, patients in ALL groups experienced significant improvement, despite the third group having no real treatment whatsoever[10].

I mention the placebo effect throughout the book, because I find the above and similar studies fascinating examples of the power of the mind, i.e. that someone can convince themselves treatment is making a physical difference when it is all psychological. You can harness this same ability to trick the body to heal and use it to overcome your anxiety.

In the words of Theodore Roosevelt, "Believe you can and you are halfway there."

Consider too that considerable scientific research has been invested into understanding the psychology of mind, what makes us tick or motivates us to action. Why, for example, do positive thoughts drive positive action and behaviour, yet limiting beliefs appear to limit our capabilities?

If I asked you to walk across a plank placed on the ground, it would cause you no problem at all. But put that same plank 100 metres in the air, it suddenly becomes a death-defying feat. A host of conflicting thought processes must be tackled to view that seemingly death-defying feat in a different light. It is these conflicting thought processes that I am interested in and the reason I devised a programme to help you identify, tackle and overcome any that may be associated with your anxiety.

Drugs are very helpful, and I recognise in some instances, vital. (Incidentally, if you are on medication, please do not come off them without first carefully consulting with your doctor or medical practitioner). However, having been through this myself without drugs, I want to show how you can rely on the power of your mind alone, should you wish to take a drug-free route. If you make this programme an ongoing part of your daily routine, the change will be noticeable and long-lasting.

The main aim of this book is to show that you already have the power within you to create a life free from chronic anxiety. But your recovery will require a change in mindset and a commitment to that change. I know it will not be easy, as the mind wants to take the path of least resistance. This is not a flaw, it is simply the way the mind prefers to work. But both mind and thoughts can be retrained.

However, this training is aimed at more than just anxiety. It will allow you to work and live 'in the zone', the state of mind where you learn to trust your instinct and not feel you must second-guess everything. You will feel free to focus on the task at hand and stride forward confidently.

Take small steps at first and keep going until you have completed the journey. Use this book to arm yourself with the new strategies within to help you challenge what might have been years of self-limiting, disquieting thoughts. In time, you WILL have a quieter, calmer mind.

"The journey of a thousand miles begins with a single step." Lao Tzu.

Roger Federer did not become one of the greatest tennis players without training. Mozart could not have written beautiful symphonies without years of practice. I will explain to you how and indeed why this programme works, but my challenge to you is simple. Will you give me just 15 minutes of your time each day for 14 days?

You have nothing to lose and everything to gain.

To your continued health and with sincerest best wishes.

Tim Patch

How to get the most from this book

I have written this book to be as informative as possible, with firstly, scientific research to support the theory behind the programme and secondly, training exercises you can use to practice the theory. It has been divided into the following sections:

Section One: Understanding fear and anxiety - the basics

Section One covers the basics of how and why anxiety happens. I also explain which regions of the brain are involved, so that you can see what impact the training has on them. These are mainly:

- the thalamus: which relays sensory information (i.e. sight, sound, taste and touch), to the cortex;

- the cortex: the wrinkly, outermost layer of the brain, divided into four lobes responsible for processing the meaning of sensory information; also responsible for thinking and planning;

- the amygdala: responsible for processing emotions and emotional memory. It plays a key role in the fear/anxiety emotion; and finally,

- the hippocampus: mainly responsible for learning and memory recall.

The reason I go into detail about these regions of the brain, is because you need to understand how they operate in anxious situations, so you can fully grasp how reversing this negative state causes real, lasting change for the better.

Section Two: Overcoming anxiety – a case for training the mind

In Section Two, you will learn that the brain is capable of dynamic change – referred to as neuroplasticity – and how you can rewire your brain to react differently to situations that would normally cause you anxiety. I cannot stress enough the importance of this concept. This is a real case for training the mind.

We know Olympic athletes spend years on physical training to perform at their optimum. However, they spend as much time on improving mental stamina. In fact, it is only possible for them to succeed because they have learned how to reduce anxiety, stress and distractions. For an athlete, this is 'playing in the zone', and a well-known mantra is "90 percent mental, 10 percent physical."

The good news is you do not need to spend years on this training. You will see later that it can be practiced within minutes in the comfort of your own home, and you already have what you need to do this, namely:

- The conscious mind: You will learn how you consciously create thoughts in the cortex. By the time you become aware of these thoughts, they will be a logical, coherent running commentary of what you are experiencing in that given moment (for example, you are probably thinking this very sentence while you read it). You will

17

discover the link between consciously created thoughts and anxiety, and how to finally break that link.

- The unconscious/subconscious mind: What causes you to blink, wiggle your fingers, move your muscles, walk, run, etc? Or what keeps your immune system ticking along? These are all automatic functions that none of us give any conscious thought to. Your mind instinctively knows how to process them behind the scenes, in what scientists call the unconscious mind. This is where you process your emotions, memories and behaviour. Where you internalise the ideals and beliefs you hold dear. One could say your unconscious mind is the storehouse of your character, defining who you are.

However, this is where the topic of the mind becomes a fascinating one, because your character will have been (and will continue to be) subconsciously influenced by a host of factors throughout your life. For this reason, I delve into the realm of the subconscious mind, and how it affects everything you think say and do. You subconsciously soak up everything, whether good, bad, positive or negative. You could almost liken your subconscious mind to an evaluation system, one that constantly weighs up whatever influences you, to then use it to make split second decisions throughout the day. You will learn how to re-train your subconscious mind so you can think and act confidently without anxiety going forward.

Section Three: The training programme in detail

Section Three is the crux of the book, with exercises containing powerful strategies you can implement from day one. Each exercise has the following phases:

- Meditation phase: to help you reach a deep, relaxed, meditative state. Anxiety causes busy thoughts to race through your mind, at times on an incessant loop. This is 'monkey mind', one that will not stop chattering. The meditation phase will allow you to break the noise to experience true calm.

- Self-hypnosis phase: for a deeper state of relaxation to help you prepare your mind for change. This phase will allow you to focus on an idea or concept to the exclusion of everything else around you. Holding this focus will not only allow a deeper state of calm, but will prepare your mind to be reprogrammed in the final visualisation phase. You may have seen a hypnotherapist help a client reach a deep trance-like relaxed state. This is simply to help the client focus on the therapist's carefully crafted suggestions to overcome a specific challenge. However, the ability to reach any depth of relaxation lies purely in the power of the person under hypnosis, not the therapist. Self-hypnosis is simply the ability to reach that state of relaxation yourself, and something you can do with practice.

- Visualisation phase: guided imagery to help you visualise a new, desired outcome. This all-important visualisation phase will reprogram your mind to think differently about the cause of your anxiety. A phrase you will see often throughout this book is 'a picture is worth a thousand words'. Visualising an image in all its technicolour glory has a far more lasting effect on the mind than simply reading about it. This makes visualisation a powerful and, in my opinion, under-utilised technique.

There are common ways in which anxiety can present challenges in everyday life. To help you overcome them, I have created 12 carefully scripted visualisation exercises in the following 7 categories:

- Achieving clarity: An anxious mind causes a circular pattern of chattering, worrying thoughts, leaving you mentally 'foggy' and unable to think clearly or act decisively. This exercise shows you how to break that cycle to achieve true clarity of mind. It also acts as a perfect primer for the remaining exercises.

- Overcoming self-consciousness and eradicating pre-judgment: Prolonged anxiety leads to heightened self-consciousness, the feeling that everyone is negatively judging you. This in turn, results in a lack of confidence or low self-esteem. There are two exercises to help you alter your perception of yourself, so you can confidently move forward in life.

- Accepting what you can or cannot control: There are countless situations in life that are outside your control, from every day annoyances to major tragedies. If you have ever found yourself worrying excessively over things you cannot control – what I refer to as 'what ifs' – these exercises will help you accept that you can safely let go of control where appropriate.

- Coping with impermanence: There are two exercises to help you accept the reality of loss, how to deal with life's changes, and how to move forward despite them. There is also an exercise to help you find peace and comfort in times of loss.

- Accepting the concept of failure: No-one wants to fail. However, if the idea of failure seems so frightening that you will do anything to avoid it, this exercise will help you accept failure as a constant in life, and perhaps more importantly, a precursor to success.

- Visualising success: Closely related to a fear of failure is a fear of success. If you are consistently shielding yourself from failing, then you are subconsciously sabotaging your efforts to succeed. This exercise is designed to help you confidently own success.

- Trust your body to live and work in the zone: This may seem an unusual exercise, as after all, the book is dedicated to freeing your anxious mind. However, a well-known expression I use throughout is, 'being in the zone'. This refers to a state of mind that allows you to carry out a task or decision without stalling or second guessing yourself. Being in the zone is the ultimate in living a life free from chronic worry or anxiety. This exercise is designed to show you how to trust your mind and body to do its job. It is the culmination of everything you will have learned throughout the book.

The main premise behind the training is to reprogram the way you think about the cause of your fears and anxiety. It will become a new technique you can use to unlearn those fears, and indeed rethink the way you approach other challenges going forward.

Jung said, "Everyone carries a shadow. It forms an unconscious snag, thwarting our most well-meant intentions."

If you regularly practice the exercises, you will quickly remove the dark shadow-like challenges commonly encountered in anxiety. The more you train, the better focused and clearer your mind will be.

Section Four: Summary and moving forward

This final section is a summary of everything you will have learned, and how to continue moving forward confidently.

I realise it will be tempting to jump straight to the training exercises without reading the theory, but I urge you to read the theory first so you understand why the training works.

You must reprogram your mind to think differently about life's challenges so that you stop becoming anxious over bumps in your path. Athletes first train to learn a correct technique – which invariably involves unlearning bad habits – then they go on to practice what they have learned so they can excel in their sport. Similarly, you will need to change your mindset, then practice what you have learned so you can continue progressing.

I have one final comment to make before we dive in. I refer to several scientific experiments throughout the book, which in some instances are detailed. While I have simplified them wherever possible, I feel that the only way to effectively explain how the brain and mind can be reprogrammed to overcome anxiety, is to give you at least some scientific background on it. The theory is fascinating and the practical extremely effective, but overall it is not a quick fix.

If like me, you enjoy watching DIY renovation programs on the television, you will know that occasionally, renovators come across a beautiful period property built before modern lighting and appliances were installed as standard. These homes will often have electrical wiring and fittings that need updating. When someone comes across a situation like this, they can either upgrade switches and circuit breakers (a quick and cheaper option), or opt for full rewiring to replace old for new.

This is the equivalent of the full rewiring. It will take time and patience, but the effects will be longer lasting.

Schedule time alone so you can become familiar with each exercise without interruption. Do this every day and you will soon find you can skilfully run through the exercises without reading them. Stick to the programme for 14 days and you will notice a marked improvement in the way you react to situations that would normally cause you anxiety.

As George Dana Boardman said, "Sow an act and you reap a habit, sow a habit and you reap a character, sow a character and you reap destiny."

MY STORY

I wish I could say I once scored the winning goal at the World Cup, acted the final scene of Macbeth at the National Theatre, danced at Covent Garden, or played lead guitarist in a rock band while touring across the States. Even second guitarist would do.

My only claim to fame is 20 years of money broking in the City of London, and made it out with my liver intact!

I had a happy childhood, played a huge amount of sport, studied (a bit), slept (a lot), ate healthy food, had good mates and had loads of fun. Frankly, I did not want for anything (other than the Adidas Stan Smith tennis shoes that were all the rage back then).

At school, we had exams every week. They fell into the category of 'stuff' we were meant to get on with, so I did not get nervous about them. I knew I had to work hard because I could see a correlation between putting in the effort and obtaining decent results.

If I did well, I got a "well done". If I did badly, it was not the end of the world. There was one occasion when my mum was not too pleased with my 20-something percent in a Latin exam. But even then, I seem to remember we were not in the car long before I escaped to the football pitch. By the next day, it was all forgotten and what seemed more important was making sure I said "hello" politely to the headmaster

Sports and a fear of failure

My earliest memory of anxiety was in my mid- to late-teens, when I began playing my two favourite sports, football and tennis. It was then that I experienced the sheer thrill and exhilaration of winning.

Tennis is not dissimilar to one-on-one combat. While the players are not physically wrestling each other, it is a fight. Watch any professional tennis player and note the violent fury with which the ball is slugged across the court. Each player is determined to take out the opponent with force.

As for the beautiful game, the team spirit among players is a shared philosophy for how they will play the game. A cohesive and co-ordinated game among a band of brothers, defending against the opposition. The enemy!

Winning felt good. Literally. But I was so desperate to win, I would worry for hours before going onto the football pitch or before playing a tennis match. My mind would churn. "What if I fail? What if I miss? How will I look? What will they think?" It was a situation I felt I could not control, which of course made me feel out of control.

(Incidentally, the desire to feel completely in control is common in anxiety, as it is akin to feeling safe. Yet it can be unhelpful, as there are limits to what anyone can control. We will tackle how to overcome a warped perception of control later.)

In the UK, 1 in 10 children have a diagnosable mental health disorder - roughly 3 children in every classroom. Half of all mental health problems manifest themselves by the age of 14, with 75% by the age of 24. (Young Minds).[1]

I did not have the luxury of statistics back then, nor did I have any inkling that I should get help, even if I knew where to obtain it. All I knew was that my raging mind would not quieten from a persistent goading to do well 'or else'. I only felt a sense of relief after a game or match had finished.

Social anxiety and panic attacks

I found more reasons to be anxious in my late teens, feeling constantly on edge in social situations. It is not unusual for teens to feel socially awkward, but my shyness was crippling. I worked hard at school but would not speak up in class. If my parents had a dinner party and we were expected to simply greet friends with a polite "hello", I would hide in my bedroom, trembling safely out of view.

I awoke every morning in angst, either fearing the day ahead of me or fretting over potential scenarios, agonising over what to say or do if something arose. It took tremendous effort to psych myself up for the simplest of tasks. Even then, I found it hard to participate because of acute shyness thinking everyone was judging me.

To make things worse, I developed hyperhidrosis – profuse sweating – not exactly what any teenage lad wants when he is trying to impress a girl for the first time. Nowadays there are cures, but back then it was embarrassing. I felt and probably looked a mess.

Anxiety robs you of clarity of mind. In one week, I was knocked out of the county tennis tournament I was seeded to win. I also failed one of my A levels. I eventually retook the exam and passed, but both experiences felt emotionally wounding.

I only passed the A level re-sit because my dad taught me an essay technique which made it easier for me to put my thoughts clearly on paper. It was the technique that saw me through, not necessarily my knowledge. I had after all messed up despite studying hard and knowing all the facts. Similarly, Free the Mind training is very much about showing you a new technique, one that shows you how to empty your mind from disquieting thoughts.

I was bound for Manchester University soon after, the home of Manchester United my other 'love'. Textiles, economics and management were going to take a back seat. I felt buoyed and optimistic.

But the second day into university life, I stepped into the student hall only to be halted by one of the most frightening experiences of my life. A vice-like cramp gripped my head with a sudden violent spasm and shook my body for what seemed like minutes (but was probably only seconds), before quickly disappearing. Suffice to say, it frightened the living daylights out of me. But as I had spent years suffering disquieting thoughts in silence, I simply composed myself as best I could and carried on with the rest of the day, thinking nothing more of it.

It happened again later that evening. And the next day. And the next day after that.

Those spasms plagued me almost every day throughout my three years at university. I suspect they occurred because my posture was poor while studying. It was also a time when I was at my most tense. Their intensity, which caused a crippling stiffness in my neck and back, convinced me something was wrong. I went to see a physiotherapist and had a few ultrasound treatments but saw no difference (other than a gaping hole in my finances).

I was a goalkeeper for the university first team in the Lancashire league, with apprentices playing for the likes of Manchester United, Manchester City, Liverpool and Everton. But matches were too much of an ordeal. By that time, I was suffering regular panic attacks with shaky limbs. Not exactly the best skill for trying to save a shot! Reluctantly I gave it all up, a sad end to my football career.

(I realise not everyone who has anxiety has panic attacks, so it is worth mentioning how they may manifest themselves. A panic attack is a rapid build-up of symptoms that often occurs with little warning. One minute you may feel perfectly fine and the next, your heart will start to pound, you feel unable to breathe – almost as if you are going to suffocate – and your throat feels tight and constricted. You start to sweat, feel clammy, faint or even nauseous. Your limbs start to shake until you feel as if you will fall over. These symptoms are so intense and rapid that the experience is utterly terrifying, and you feel out of control. The more you focus on the symptoms, the worse you feel. In all, a distressing experience. If you suffer from panic attacks, be assured they can be controlled effectively, as I explain later).

Academically I did okay, but would panic for days before a presentation, fearing a repeat of my episodes – the vice-like grip around my head, debilitating shivers and shakes, gut-wrenching tightening within my stomach, profuse sweating, or a pounding, palpitating heart. It was frightening and embarrassing. Luckily, I managed to wriggle out of giving presentations from then on, simply going to lectures, completing my homework, and avoiding much else.

My anxiety and panic attacks increased in both frequency and intensity, which would of course annoy me and make the situation worse until I could concentrate on nothing else. I would find it hard to sit still, engrossed in an internal battle to get through even the smallest event that lay ahead. I hated this feeling of helplessness, and often found myself wondering how others seemed to get through their day with ease.

Things got to a point where I considered becoming a monk, simply as an avenue for me to escape. As odd as it might sound, that obscure thought was my saving grace, because it was while I sought a spiritual retreat of sorts that I came across an old bookshop and the solution to my problem. An inconspicuous little book called "Clear Light of Bliss."[2]

Making sense of it all

That book made complete sense. I learned I could overcome mental chatter and negativity to achieve bliss through meditation and visualisation. Bliss is often misunderstood to mean a state of elated ecstasy. However, in meditation, it relates to inner contentedness and calm. Calm was of course, exactly what I wanted to achieve.

"The only thing we have to fear is fear itself." Franklin D. Roosevelt, First Inaugural Address.

I learned there is a strong correlation between a fit, healthy mind and a fit, healthy body. As a keen sportsman, I could relate to this. A tennis player will put hours of practice into perfecting his or her technique but will put just as much effort into learning how to mentally outsmart their opponent. Similarly, a footballer will train for physical strength, agility and speed but will spend just as much time 'reading' the opposing players' moves.

Look at the displays of Shaolin monks. Certainly, hours of physical training will have gone into their amazing performances. But perhaps even more time will have been spent allowing their mind to be free from negative self-talk. They must be in the zone so that there is no doubt they can achieve the task at hand.

I finally understood that I needed a radical transformation of mind and thought. Just as a sportsman must replace unhealthy habits with new ones, I had to replace years of unhelpful, negative thoughts with healthy positive ones. Thoughts that could move me forward and help me get on with my life instead of holding me back. It soon dawned on me how fascinated I was in understanding the workings of the mind and the brain. It was a subject I wanted to explore further.

Looking back, I will be ever thankful for finding that book. It spurred me on to research the benefits of meditation and later, self-hypnosis and visualisation. I devised a simple programme where I trained for half an hour, twice a day every day. I never missed a session. The better I felt, the more it spurred me on to continue.

It was an early phase in developing the training, so I was still anxious and could not, for example, hold down a job while at University. I was probably up against so many others who had better interview skills than me. However, I was clearly heading upstream to a better destination, because when I left University, I got a job as dustman. Okay, so it was a humble job, but it meant I could start early in the morning, then get back home in good time to do my training.

The training soon enabled me to become calmer and focused. Before long, I secured a job at an investment house in Kent and could by then, sit 9-10 hours a day, talk to people in meetings, give presentations and live a normal life without the daily butterflies in my stomach. I felt let out of jail, finally able to free the heavy chains of anxiety weighing me down.

I stuck with the training. I would not have managed the rigours of a career in the city without it.

A career in the city puts Free the Mind training to the test

"The best way out is always through." Robert Frost.

It was by now the 1990s. Having received a pile of rejections from practically every institution in the city, I finally received a letter requesting my presence for an interview. Suited and booted, I turned up eager for the interview and was taken through the dealing floor into an office full of men shouting, swearing and chanting. It sounded more like Stretford End, the West Stand at Old Trafford Stadium, than a professional office.

The first interview question was, "Can you shout?" Given that I had been to interviews at merchant banks where oil paintings lined the wall and people drank tea from bone china teacups, this seemed an unusual approach. I replied that I used to be a goalkeeper ordering defences around. It seemed to be the correct answer, so I was then asked if I wanted to earn the same amount of money as one of the directors in the room. This was ten times my proposed starting salary! Again, I answered positively, just wanting an opportunity to have a shot at a great career.

The next question was whether I had a problem with going out late in the evening. I could hardly reply that my mum wanted me back home in bed by 8.30pm. Nowadays, interns are put through their paces in the style of television's 'The Apprentice' just to be considered for the role. Yet, there I was being asked whether I could shout, stay out late, or work till the wee hours of the morning.

The interview was finally topped with a stern warning. I was told there was one strict rule which, if broken, would lead to immediate disciplinary action. I expected to be given a book crammed with

31

company rules and regulations. Instead, the director looked me in the eye and commanded, "Under no circumstances must you punch anybody in the dealing room, no matter how tense the situation."

I got the job!

My first day was spent sitting in front of two computer screens, with the constant shrill of telephones around me. Brokers bellowed down telephones pasted to both ears, while gesticulating wildly on the trading floor. About an hour later, someone came in from the arbitrage desk. "Oi," he shouted across to the chap I was sitting next to at the time, "Who's the bald, ginger c**t sitting next to you, then?" I offered my hand and he laughed. It was my dubious first welcome to the world of money-broking.

Make no mistake, these guys knew how to sniff out a deal. They knew their clients paid their salary. Some brought in tens of thousands of pounds (sterling) a week in business, which meant dealing in billions of pounds as commission rates were low. Nobody could take away a broker's income without a battle. I was clear about one thing. If I brought in money to the business, I would be rewarded. If not, the door was always open.

In the trading game, speed was of the essence. The complexity of the markets and numerous other factors determining prices meant you had to think quickly on your feet. There were chains of people calling each other, with a back office settling the trade. As dealers, our job was to go back and forth between buyer and seller to negotiate a price. I would often have multiple deals in progress at any one time.

The role required split-second, precision thinking. It was not for the faint-hearted and I would not have managed it years prior with an anxious, agitating mind that catastrophised or imagined worst case scenarios. By the time I landed this role, I trusted my instincts and simply acted. Everyone knew they had to double their ticket. The bigger the deal, the more money we were paid. It required intense concentration, and I was only capable of doing it with my mind training programme.

My second welcome to money markets? Cigarette smoke-filled dealing rooms with everyone glued to their screens until lunch time, when we all took the obligatory trip to the pub. On one occasion, still new to the job, 11.30am arrived and we all milled out for lunch. I went up to the bar and asked my colleague what he would like to drink. "Beer", he responded, so I dutifully asked the barman for two bottles of Becks.

My colleague slapped me on the back and laughed, "Lad, you've got a lot to learn. In 20 minutes, the bar will be packed, and it will take ages to get another drink." He yelled across to the barman, "He means the crate, mate. Just the one. And make it sharp, we've got to get back to the office in 50 minutes." The barman dumped a crate of bottles on our table and off we started.

It was an initiation into the giddy world of wining and dining billion-dollar clients. We spoiled them, and they gave us their business. Frankly, I could tell you hundreds of tales of what went on well into the night and into the early hours of the morning, without us getting a wink of sleep.

Each floor of the building had its own identity. One of the directors wanted to bring a team of foreign exchange brokers up from another floor onto the sterling room where I worked. None of us wanted this to happen, as we knew it would impact on our bonus pool. But the director, in his wisdom, decided that a night out would create team spirit and iron out any potential problems.

Both teams met up at a pub in Covent Garden. Everything went smoothly until 10pm, when an argument broke out. Fists started flying, a major fight spilled out onto the streets, and the police were called. The next day at the office, many of the desks were empty. The director walked in, keen to find out whether his brilliant plan had worked, only to slink back to his office when he was told that half the team were either in hospital or being looked after by 'Her Majesty's Finest'. The teams never did merge.

If it sounds like every working man's dream, it was not. No one dared call in sick, no matter how heavy the entertaining the night before. The constant need to entertain clients at various locations around Europe, hustling to develop my own line of clients while working with the team to develop new technology to stay ahead of the game, was all extremely tiring. On top of that, office hours were long, often from 7am to find out what was happening on the markets, until well into the night or early hours of the next morning. The intensity and scope of the work, while hunched over a bunch of computer screens and screaming down the telephone for hours on end, meant I often had excruciating back pain.

By the late 90s, I took six months out to find a cure for my back. Massage helped a little, so I went back to another broking outfit on a weekly basis without signing a contract, paid by cheque at the end of the month just to see how I would cope. The desk was very much a start-up, so it meant more entertaining and late evenings. The progress was fun, but the crippling back pain became too much. After spending the next 12 years working for two more broking outfits and wasting thousands of pounds on medical treatments, I had no option but to call it a day.

New habits for a healthy mind and body

"I am not a product of my circumstances. I am a product of my decisions." Stephen R. Covey.

I eventually learned that stretched ligaments in my upper back were causing the spasms and was advised to stop looking for a cure but to do regular stretching exercises and swim to alleviate the pain. I am thankfully pain-free nowadays, and although swimming is not my favourite activity, I swim every day as it is perfect for toning and strengthening the back muscles.

Shortly after I left the City, I had plenty of time to reflect on my career up to that point. My career as a broker spanned twenty years. Few people survive the intensity of such a stressful career for that length of time. I would not have been able to manage it without Free the Mind training. If anything, the training positively helped my career.

For a start, because I had in the past felt permanently nervous and uptight, I would not have been able to sit in the same place for hours on end, nor act instinctively without second-guessing myself. As a money broker, one is dealing with huge deals worth hundreds of millions, if not billions of dollars. The larger the trade, the bigger the bonus at the end. Without the training, I would no doubt, have spent hours stressing about whether I had made a mistake during a trade and the possible repercussions.

In the 90s trading transactions were carried out over the telephone in a large trading floor full of noise. It was very easy to simply not to hear everything being said by a trader. Transactions were written on pieces of paper and thrown into a tray. It was no more formal than that. How more mistakes did not happen, heaven only knows. I had however, created visualisation techniques to make me subconsciously aware that there was little I could do if I had made a mistake, and to not dwell on 'what-ifs' but simply move onto the next trade.

In money broking we did not get many shots anyway. Our line list would probably be traders within 4 or 5 banks minimum. In years gone by, I would have fretted about what my colleagues thought about me (probably with good reason, as I was obsessed with talking about Manchester United and the midfield prowess of Paul Scholes). But the new techniques I had learned, enabled me to accept I had no real idea what people thought of me. There is much in life that no-one can control, and it was pointless worrying about it.

I had also been incredibly self-conscious as a teenager, even walking into a packed supermarket would have made me feel uncomfortable. Yet there I was as a broker, shouting orders across a trading floor. It was only possible because I had learned to use specific techniques to alleviate self-consciousness and accept that the world is a massive place, with people far too busy looking after their own affairs than to even notice me. There is a lot to be said about not thinking negatively and having true clarity of mind.

One of the other challenges I had to contend with my back problem and stretched ligaments, was that aside from the pain, I would experience spasms and tremors. The environment on the trading floor was extremely competitive and there were days when I missed countless deals. However, Free the Mind training made it much easier to manage the competitive nature of my job despite these setbacks.

The fear of failure is extremely counter-productive. It holds you back instead of propelling you forward. I used the training to change a negative mindset full of misconceptions, to one that was positive and optimistic. I taught myself to accept that I learned far more from competing, than I did from trying to avoid failure altogether.

I would never have imagined, as a teenager, that I could become a money broker. I feel incredibly fortunate to have managed to get 20 years out of such a rewarding career.

The training has also brought home to me how vital it is to treat body and mind holistically. This training has given me the confidence to pursue what I really want in life, and it is my hope that it can help you do the same. I now split my time between trading wine, working with an old friend from my money broking days, and helping others overcome their anxiety.

I am not a psychologist or a psychotherapist or a guru who organises exclusive 'all secrets revealed' retreats. I am just a regular guy who has spent years developing a training programme that banishes unwanted, anxious, negative chatter. It has helped others and my hope is that it will help you too.

The aim of the training is to clear your mind so that you are free to focus. This will feel awkward at first. After all, have you ever had a mind that is entirely free from thought? Most of your thoughts may have been negative or focused on worries over which you have no control. But I am going to help you clear away the negative rubble so that your mind is free and calm, ready for the day ahead.

When you start training, it will feel strange to clear your mind in this way, but once you have learned to do so, you will never look back. It is a beautiful, empowering feeling. When I was sitting in the classroom unable to concentrate for hours on end concerned that I might not play well or would let in a goal, the beliefs were preconditioned. The more I thought about trying to get rid of these chains of worry, the more they bounced back and made things worse. In the end just playing a simple game of football for the school felt like a six-hour endurance sport. The training thankfully gave me a ladder to get out of what felt like a trap, and more besides.

As I said earlier, the first book I ever studied on overcoming anxiety was a tremendous find and set me on the right path. I hope this book will do the same for you, as having a chattering, negative, anxious mind is destructive.

I feel honoured to pass Free the Mind training on to you now, and know that if you apply the training, it WILL work.

So, if you are ready, shall we begin?

SECTION ONE
UNDERSTANDING ANXIETY, THE BASICS

The first step to overcoming anxiety is understanding what it is. In Section One, I explain:

- the difference between fear and anxiety;

- how anxiety is usually triggered by:

  - the amygdala, plus examples of amygdala-based anxiety; and,

  - the cortex, with examples of cortex-based anxiety.

Now you will have to forgive me for the scientific references in this section. Humans are only born with two fears (of falling and of loud noises [1&2]. All other fears are learned (conditioned). It is helpful to know this because it means unhelpful fears can be unlearned.

We will explore what goes on inside the brain when something either frightens you straight away – which is not necessarily a bad thing – or when you become anxious because of fear conditioning.

Fear and anxiety - the basics

The words fear and anxiety are often used interchangeably, which is not surprising, as they both have similar symptoms. However, there are differences between them, and understanding those differences will help you manage them effectively when they arise.

What is fear?

Fear is a basic response to danger. Your body is so finely tuned to the threat of danger, that when you sense it, a defence mechanism reacts instinctively. Without this mechanism, you would not be able to protect yourself effectively.

For the sake of simplicity, the fear response involves mainly (but not exclusively), the following regions of the brain:

- **the thalamus:** relays sensory information (i.e. sight, sound, taste and touch), to the cortex;

- **the cortex:** the wrinkly, outermost layer of the brain, divided into four lobes, each responsible for processing the meaning of sensory information;

- **the amygdala:** responsible for emotions and emotional memories. It plays a key role in the fear/anxiety emotion; and

- **the hippocampus:** mainly responsible for learning and memory recall.

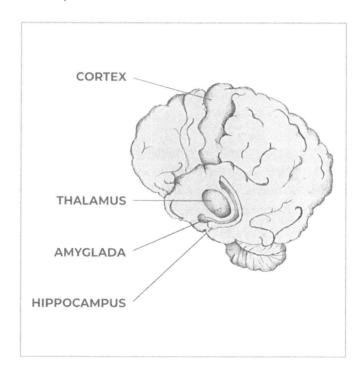

Figure 1:THE ANATOMY OF FEAR

41

the fear response also involves:

- **the sympathetic nervous system:** designed to accelerate the heart rate, raise blood pressure and give a burst of energy; and

- **the parasympathetic nervous system:** designed to slow down the heart rate, relax the muscles and conserve energy.

To illustrate how these regions operate and interact when you experience fear, imagine the following scenario. You are walking home alone on a dark night, you hear a loud crash and are so startled by the noise, you jump and freeze.

Your thalamus responsible for processing sensory information, will process the loud crashing noise to your cortex, to interpret its meaning as 'danger'. Jumping and freezing in this context is a classic, instinctive response and difficult to control.

Meanwhile, your amygdala responsible for processing emotions, will process 'danger' as a fear emotion and will automatically trigger the sympathetic nervous system, designed to accelerate your heart rate and give you a burst of energy. Your heart will pound, you will feel hot and clammy, and you will begin to panic.

While these symptoms might not feel very pleasant, they are an amazing cascade of actions designed to give your body a surge of energy should you decide to run in the opposite direction or stand your ground to fight and defend yourself.

Of course, you might have a quick look round and realise there is no danger. In which case, your cortex will interpret the situation as 'safe'. Your amygdala will in turn, process this 'safe emotion' by triggering the parasympathetic system to calm you down. Your heart rate will slow down, and you will eventually regain composure.

As you can see from this scenario, the fear response is perfectly normal. It is an instinctive, automatic response, designed to protect your body from literal harm or imminent danger. It is commonly referred to as the fight/flight response, an expression you will see throughout the book.

What is anxiety?

Not all fears, however, are a result of literal danger. Some are learned, and this is where fear can become conditioned, leading to anxiety.

Research shows, for example, that children from as early as seven learn to fear creepy crawlies if they observe their friends responding fearfully to them[1]. Research also indicates that children are more likely to develop phobias if their parents have a phobia.[2]

Fear can also become conditioned by instruction. One study was conducted in which participants were told they would receive a mild electric shock to the wrist, but only when they were shown a blue square. Although no shocks were given, whenever the blue square was shown, the participants had the fight/flight response.[3]

This shows we can fear something by association. If we associate feeling afraid with what we think is the cause of that fear, it will cause anxiety. How many people, for example, fear great white sharks even though they have never seen one in real life? They may have heard about shark bites third-hand and seen images of shark bite marks third-hand. This seems to be enough to condition the mind that great white sharks are something to fear, (and if you have ever watched 'Jaws' the movie, you will understand exactly what I mean).

Preconditioned beliefs are significant players in anxiety. The key to overcoming anxiety is to challenge those beliefs.

So, anxiety bears similarities to fear, but where fear is to a clear and literal danger, anxiety arises in response to internal conflict. There is no literal danger.

Yet you and I know that when your heart starts to pound wildly, or your throat becomes so constricted you can hardly breathe, none of those symptoms are imaginary. So, why does an anxiety attack feel so real?

Because it triggers the same regions of the brain that are triggered during the fear response.

Here is a scenario to illustrate what I mean.

'Brian' has heard there are threats of redundancy in his workplace. His mind begins to trace all the mistakes he thinks he may have made or colleagues and bosses he may have upset. He worries his past sins will catch up with him and feels certain he will be one of the first to be selected for redundancy. Panic sets in as he conjures an image of himself sitting at home, out of work and unable to pay his bills or provide for his family. His heart beats wildly, his face and palms feel hot and clammy and he begins to have a panic attack. He feels so unwell, he decides to take a day off sick – which worries him even further.

As you can see from this scenario, there is no literal threat or danger to cause Brian physical harm, yet his anxiety has triggered the fight/flight symptoms. The longer Brian dwells on the cause of his anxiety, the more unwell he will feel, because he is 'training' (conditioning) his mind to stay in a heightened state of anxiety.

The key to finding out why anxiety mimics fear in this way is to identify where anxiety is triggered, and it is usually the amygdala or the cortex.

I discuss this in the following chapters. But first, a quick summary.

Summary

There is a difference between fear and anxiety.

Fear occurs when the brain detects literal danger and prompts the amygdala into action, the fight/flight response. It is quick, instinctive and designed to protect your body from literal harm.

Anxiety, on the other hand is a learned, conditioned response which causes internal conflict. It can, however, mimic fear triggering similar fight/flight symptoms.

You can learn how to overcome anxiety by identifying where it is triggered – either the cortex or the amygdala.

How anxiety is triggered by the amygdala

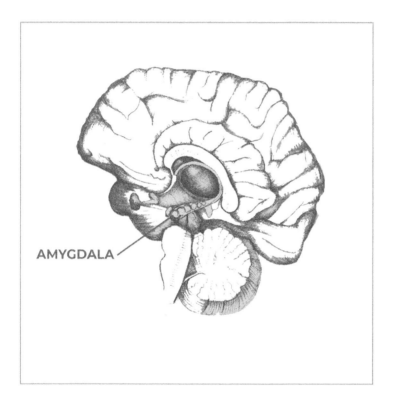

Figure 2: THE AMYGDALA

The amygdala is a small, almond-shaped region of the brain, responsible for decoding and processing emotions. I am focusing here on the fear/anxiety emotions, but it also processes jealousy, anger, envy and grief. It also stores memories based on emotional experiences.

From an evolutionary perspective, the amygdala was hardwired to protect the body from literal, environmental harm[1]. In the context of a prehistoric world, the amygdala had to quickly react to protect primitive man from snakes, bears and fearsome sabre-toothed tigers. The fight/flight response would have quite literally been a matter of survival.

Of course, we no longer grapple with prehistoric animals to survive, yet the amygdala is still eagerly waiting to respond to what it perceives as danger. Think of your amygdala as a very alert, conscientious guard who takes his job very seriously. Whenever you become anxious, he springs into action. Picture him jumping up and down shouting, "Danger! Danger! For Pete's sake, RUN!"

As this little fellow is nestled so deep within your brain, you often feel anxious long before you understand why. Have you, for example, ever experienced a startle response when you thought you saw something scuttle across the room just out of eye shot?

Remember, your thalamus plays a key role in processing sensory information and relaying it to your amygdala to decode it as either safe or dangerous. This route from thalamus to amygdala is quick and instinctive. It needs to be, to protect you from potential 'harm'. So, not surprisingly, an unfamiliar or unpredictable experience can elicit a startle-like response, whether the response is a general:

"Eww! What on earth was that?"

to something that feels unsettling within a social context,

"I feel so uncomfortable in this situation, get me out of here."

This brings me to something I briefly referred to earlier, a panic attack. It is a classic example of amygdala-based anxiety, where you

47

feel anxious and panicky long before you can understand why. The subtle difference with a panic attack, however, is that symptoms are often intense and rapid:

- your heart pounds so heavily you feel unable to breathe;

- your throat feels tight and constricted or you feel as if you will suffocate;

- you start to sweat and feel clammy;

- you feel faint, nauseous and your limbs start to shake;

- you may feel dizzy, light headed and out of control as if you will fall over.

The effects can leave a lasting, negative toll on you, because you remember the intense fear and terror of the attack, which affects your self-confidence. You then feel anxious and tense about having another attack, so you avoid situations you think could trigger another one.

You feel this way because after a panic attack (and similarly, after a normal anxiety attack), your amygdala is on full alert, in a heightened state of security. Imagine your little guard, all heckles raised, eagerly poised for action just in case that dangerous *thing* comes back again!

Put simply, your amygdala needs to calm down. You need to find a way to 'show' it that some things – the cause of your anxiety – are not necessarily life threatening at all.

You do this by changing the way you respond to situations that would normally cause you anxiety, and in so doing, condition your amygdala to behave more appropriately in future.

I explain how to do this later, but at least you now understand why your amygdala behaves – or misbehaves – in the way that it does.

Examples of amygdala-based anxiety

It may be helpful for you to identify if your anxiety is amygdala-based. Can you relate to any of the following statements?

I sometimes feel scared, panicky or worried, for no apparent reason.

I feel uncomfortable in certain places/situations, but I don't understand why.

I'm often unable to control my emotional reactions.

I don't know what triggers my anxiety, it just seems to happen out of nowhere.

This is not intended to be an exhaustive list of symptoms, but simply common ones I have found in my experience of helping others overcome amygdala-based anxiety. If you can relate to these symptoms, be assured that the training will help you overcome them.

Summary

Your amygdala is hard wired to protect your body from what it perceives as literal harm or danger. However, at times, it gets things wrong by reacting to something that is not literally dangerous. This type of anxiety means you often feel anxious long before you understand why.

Whenever you react anxiously to a situation, you are conditioning your amygdala – your conscientious little guard – to spring into action to protect you.

You can, however, overcome amygdala-based anxiety by changing the way you respond to situations that would normally cause you anxiety, and train your amygdala to 'learn' how to react more appropriately in future.

How anxiety is triggered by the cortex

The role of the cortex is to interpret the world around you when it processes sensory information – sight, sound, taste and touch.

It can only interpret the meaning of things through context and association. So, for example, the crashing sound in our dark night scenario referred to earlier, is either interpreted as danger in the context of a situation you have not had chance to evaluate (it is dark, after all), or alternatively, as safe once you have had chance to evaluate it as such.

The cortex processes information slowly and deliberately, in comparison to the speedy, instinctive amygdala. It makes sense that this process is slower, when you consider the cortex is where planning, thinking, logic and conscious memory happens – skills that require careful deliberation.

The problem is, however, the cortex can produce thoughts or images that are not necessarily based on fact. When it does, those thoughts or images can be misinterpreted as distressing. The amygdala – your conscientious little guard – is eagerly waiting for anything it perceives as dangerous. So, guess what distressing thoughts or images are processed as? Yes, fear, which of course results in the fight/flight response.

If we go back to Brian's scenario mentioned earlier, his mind traces all the mistakes he thinks he may have made – not necessarily based on fact – which leads him to generate other negatives thoughts and ideas not based on fact. This creates a snowball effect. The more he dwells on negative ideas, the more distressed he becomes until he has a full-blown anxiety attack.

The ability to generate multiple thoughts and ideas in this way is not necessarily a bad thing. In fact, it can be useful. Thanks to frontal lobes located at the front of your cortex, you can generate multiple thoughts and ideas to solve problems, imagine the future, or envisage the outcome of something[1].

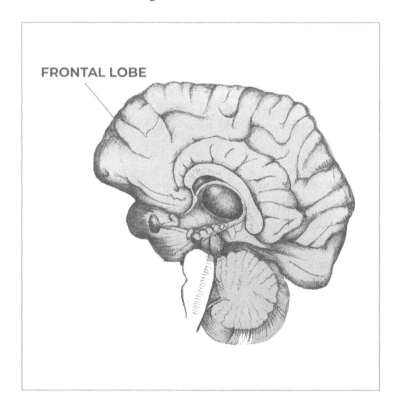

Figure 3: FRONTAL LOBE

However, in Brian's case, he has allowed that initial snowball of worry to run unchecked until it has generated an avalanche of anxiety.

He needs a strategy he can use to reframe the way he thinks about challenging situations – in this case, the threat of redundancy – to stop worry in its tracks. I explain what that strategy is later, but now you know why and how thoughts can lead to cortex-based anxiety.

Examples of Cortex-Based Anxiety

As before, it may be helpful for you to identify if your anxiety is cortex-based. Can you relate to any of the following?

You think of scenarios that will turn out badly for you.

You have upsetting thoughts or images that pop into your head without warning.

You can imagine ways in which you might embarrass yourself.

You spend a lot of time worrying about potential/past mistakes.

You often worry about things that can go wrong.

You constantly ask, "What if...?"

Once again, this is not an exhaustive list of symptoms, but simply pointers you can use to help identify what might be a tendency towards cortex-based anxiety. I discuss how to overcome cortex-based anxiety in the following chapters.

Summary

Unlike amygdala-based anxiety which is felt, cortex-based anxiety is all thought.

The cortex can produce thoughts or images that are not necessarily based on fact. These can, in turn be interpreted as distressing, which alerts the amygdala to trigger the fight/flight response.

Be assured that you can overcome cortex-based anxiety by reframing your thoughts. This will prevent the snowball effect of initial negative ideas running away unchecked and becoming an avalanche of anxiety, triggering unpleasant anxiety symptoms.

SECTION TWO: OVERCOMING ANXIETY, A CASE FOR TRAINING THE MIND

In Section Two, I explain:

- why it is vital to retrain your mind to unlearn anxiety;

- how to utilise the full breadth of your conscious and subconscious mind;

- an introduction to the strategies you can use to overcome amygdala- and cortex-based anxiety.

Why train the mind?

You are probably familiar with the analogy that likens the mind to software code and the brain to the computer in which it resides. It is a nice simple analogy, but one that does not do justice to the complexity of either mind or brain.

With our mind we manifest thoughts, ideas, perception, attention, memory and imagination. We have forethought – the unique ability to imagine the future – as a result of which we can create the future we imagine. Our mind makes us uniquely human.

Our brain the most complex organ in the body 'powers' both mind and body. It controls everything we do and plays a vital role in our body's nervous system, enabling us to respond to the world around us.

The reason why I am focusing on the relationship between mind and brain here, is because your mind is powerful enough to 'rewire' your brain – i.e., to strengthen it and make it work more efficiently.

Allow me to explain in greater detail – and once again, please bear with me while I use the occasional medical term.

The very building blocks of your brain and nervous system are specialised cells called neurons and glia. Neurons are considered the most important cells which specialise in processing signals around the brain, the body's nervous system, organs, muscles, and glands. Glia cells support and protect neurons.

Neurons are made up of three parts: (1) at one end is the nucleus and surrounding fibres, called dendrites; (2) extending from the cell body is the axon, and (3) at the end of the axon are nerve endings[1].

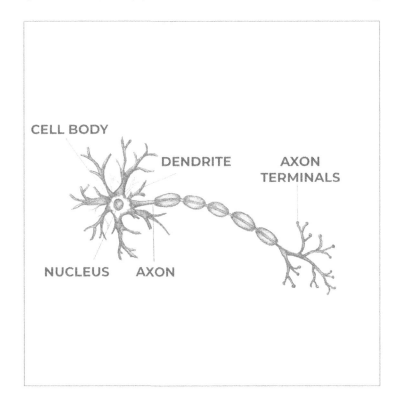

Figure 4: NEURON

Recent research suggests there are 86 billion neurons in the human brain and yet incredibly, not one of them touch each other. Each neuron is separated by a gap called a synapse. It is at this synapse 'contact' point that neurons send and receive electrical impulses to the nerve ending.[2&3]

Perhaps even more astounding is that a single neuron may send signals to thousands of neurons throughout the brain, while simultaneously receiving signals from thousands of others.

So, what is the big deal about neurons?

Scientists used to think that the brain is static and once it matures, stops growing. They also thought that once cells are damaged or die, they are gone for good. Recent research, however, shows that the brain is far from static. It is now considered to be a highly sophisticated self-organising 'system', constantly growing, changing and capable of spontaneous adaptation.

This is called neuroplasticity, the brain's ability to adapt, change or repair itself through stimulation and experience, and it is seen in two ways, by (a) forming new neurons, and/or (b) strengthening connections between neurons[4].

Research into neuroplasticity is still relatively young, only since the 1990s, but there have been fascinating studies which demonstrate neuroplasticity in action. Here are some examples:

- London licensed taxi drivers spend two to four years learning the quickest route around London's 25,000 streets, its 20,000 landmarks and its places of interest. This training is known colloquially as 'The Knowledge'. An experiment was conducted in which trainee taxi drivers were assessed before and after the training. You would expect successful trainees to have better memories. They did. But what is more interesting is that the region of the brain responsible for learning and memory recall (the hippocampus) had physically increased in volume. In other words, a growth of new neurons.[5]

- Memory loss can occur in old age, with extreme examples seen in dementia and Alzheimer's. Research has shown that this is typically down to the deterioration of the hippocampus. A study was conducted to determine whether physical exercise can prevent this deterioration from taking place. The volunteers between the ages of 59 and 81, were put through moderate cardio exercise. The results were similar to the taxi driver experiment referred to above. Volunteers had a growth in new neurons. This indicates the benefits of exercise to protect against memory loss in old age.[6]

- Long-term meditation has been shown to improve the memory of patients with depression. I highlight even more benefits of meditation later.[7&8]

- Do memory training games work? According to one study, yes. Thirty-two healthy young adult volunteers were recruited to play a selection of memory training games for 15 minutes per day, at least 5 days per week, over a period of 4 weeks (lucky volunteers). They were tested before and after for: intelligence, planning and solving problems, working memory, short-term memory, attention, processing speed, visual ability and reading ability. Results showed that the games had improved many of these functions, which shows the brain's ability to strengthen connections between neurons.[9]

- After trauma or stroke, the brain can regenerate and repair itself by neurons working in unison as a network throughout the brain. Scientists believe this repair and regeneration works by the undamaged neurons taking over the job of the dead or damaged ones.[10]

These are fascinating studies and one cannot help but look forward to further research into neuroplasticity to see whether it can be applied to staving off dementia, brain disorders, or other types of brain injury. In the meantime, these studies clearly demonstrate that the brain can adapt and change to external experience or stimulation.

These studies also show that the brain and mind operate in a symbiotic relationship, where the brain in all its power and capability, is stimulated by the mind. We see proof of this from the studies showing better memory due to acquired knowledge, abstract learning and meditation. Equally, the mind clearly benefits from a strengthened, stimulated brain.

How can this help you overcome anxiety?

Firstly, it is important to note that these changes are long-lasting only if the experience and stimulation your brain and mind are exposed to are maintained. To use a well-known expression, 'use it or lose it.' When you practice a new habit, it becomes permanent.

Secondly, if your mind can be trained to produce long-lasting changes in the brain and vice versa, what if there was a way to 'rewire' your mind and brain so that you could permanently respond far more effectively to the cause of your anxiety?

And what if doing so enabled you to live every aspect of your life – personally, professionally and socially – fully engaged, without feeling held back, ever again?

There is! And you have it here in the pages of this book. Free the Mind training has been designed to:

- through carefully designed mind training exercises, provide an entirely new experience and stimulation for your mind; and

- regulate the regions of the brain activated during anxiety, so that you respond differently when you are faced with a challenging situation.

As with any new training programme, this requires dedication and persistence to benefit from it. However, if you consistently maintain it as a newly-acquired habit, the change will be long-lasting.

So, now that you have seen why you should train your mind, in the following chapters I will explain how.

Summary

Your mind is powerful enough to 'rewire' your brain, to make it work more efficiently. This is possible because of your brain's neuroplasticity, its ability to adapt to stimulation and new experiences.

Your brain and mind operate in a symbiotic relationship where they clearly benefit from each other. Your brain is strengthened and stimulated by your mind through acquired knowledge, abstract learning and meditation. Your mind clearly benefits from a strengthened, stimulated brain.

'Use it or lose it'. When you practice a new habit, it becomes permanent. Learn the new habits in this book, practice them and maintain them going forward. When you do, the results will be long-lasting.

You already have everything you need to overcome your anxiety – the power of your mind.

The conscious mind

Your conscious mind is your objective, thinking mind. It is what you use to plan, analyse, make instant judgements, look to the future and reflect on the past. It is what you are using this very moment to take in the information you are reading, and it all happens in your cortex.

Yet, the conscious mind is surprisingly superficial.

Sigmund Freud, considered to be the founding father of psychoanalysis, was interested in the notion of the mind storing repressed memories and the effect this may have on a person's behaviour.

He developed a model of what he thought the mind's function and structure looked like, describing the mind as an iceberg with what he called 'the conscious mind' at the tip of the iceberg, 'the preconscious mind' just below it and 'the unconscious mind' deeper still. It is a useful analogy, purely to help explain the way the mind works. However, today you are more likely to see these states of mind referred to as: the conscious, the subconscious and the unconscious.

You may be surprised to learn that the conscious mind at the tip of the iceberg, has limited processing capabilities. When you consciously think, you can only do so by stringing sentence structures together in a logical, linguistic pattern, e.g. "I wonder if I should do this now? No, perhaps not. But what will happen if I don't?" Almost like a running commentary of what you experience in any given moment. (It is useful to know this, because cortex-based anxiety is very much about getting caught up in your own thoughts, often unable to break the commentary).

Yet consider what prehistoric man originally had to contend with each day to survive. There was no time for him to stop and deliberately ponder, "I wonder if that sabre-toothed tiger hurtling towards me is going to eat me. Should I throw myself on the ground and play dead? Should I run? Should I try my brand-new spear and see if it works? Oh dear! Decisions, decisions!" His tingling senses would have automatically jolted him to action.

Conscious thinking seems to have evolved out of man's need to be a member of the clan. He had to remember the rules of the clan, or what happened if he did not remember them.

Later, as he developed technical and social skills, he would have made more sophisticated decisions to express his motives, intentions or desires to share and co-operate.[1&2] You can see how in a modern world in which people must constantly weigh up the pros and cons of increasingly complex situations, this has led to a tendency to over think and over analyse, which in turn has led to anxiety.

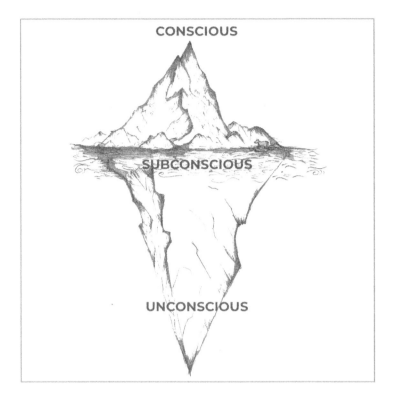

Figure 5: TOPOGRAPHY OF MIND

The challenge with getting caught up in your own mind with negative thoughts, is finding a way to break the cycle.

Challenging cortex-based anxiety by reframing negative thoughts

An immediate way to break the endless cycle of "what ifs" is to:

- challenge them,

- reframe (or modify them), then

- replace them with positive thoughts to help you move forward.

So, take for example, the self-limiting thought, "I can't get anything right. My whole life is a mess."

This can be challenged, reframed and then replaced with the following line of self-enquiry:

- Challenge: What evidence do I have to show that this is really true? What evidence do I have to show this is not true?

- Reframe/modify: How else can I view this situation? Suppose I view it positively, how will it feel/look?

- Replace: How can I change what I believe after weighing up all these factors?

This simple method of self-enquiry is commonly used in Cognitive Behavioural Therapy and can be very useful in helping you take a step back to view a challenge or situation from a different perspective.

We will, however, take this even deeper with the training. You will, for example, learn how to banish negative 'what ifs', as the training enables your mind to be clear and not ruminate. You will also understand how to not judge everything adversely and feel held back by those judgements, but rather, to take things in your stride. Overall, you will learn how to be far more positive about issues.

Exercise

What self-limiting thoughts would you like to challenge?

Why not tackle one now by using the line of self-enquiry referred to above. Work through it one step at a time. Practice doing this, and you will soon find you can challenge self-limiting thoughts without having to write them down.

Overcoming cortex-based anxiety with meditation

For longer-term reprogramming, however, the way to stop getting caught up in your own thoughts is paradoxically, to NOT try to stop them. After all, have you found whenever unwelcome thoughts enter your mind, trying to stop or suppress them is frustrating? Instead, far more helpful, is to learn how to casually observe them and allow them to simply pass by.

Imagine you went out for a walk and had to cross a busy road with noisy traffic. You would not jump into the middle of the road to try and chase the cars away, would you? You would simply stop and allow the traffic to pass by.

Unwelcome or obsessive thoughts can be likened to those noisy cars, bustling along your mind. Rather than mentally exhaust yourself by trying to chase them away, I show you how to allow unwelcome thoughts to simply pass by until you achieve true clarity. This is based on Zen meditation, the art of letting go and being completely still.

There is a Zen Proverb which says: "It is the silence between the notes that make the music."

Think of a piece of music. Would you appreciate the beauty of the music if there were no gaps between each note? Without those gaps, it would be a discordant collection of noise.

Similarly, I believe this is what happens in an anxious mind that has not yet learned to quieten it with mediation. It has accumulated so much noise - monkey mind chatter - that it has become impossible to appreciate the true beauty of the mind in between that noise.

There is also scientific proof that meditating to clear the mind in this way has powerful benefits on your power of concentration and alertness.[3] When you come out of this type mediation, you have even greater clarity and focus.

Here is a true story to illustrate the power of meditation. On June 23rd 2018, 12 young Thai footballers and their coach went to explore the Tham Luang caves in Northern Thailand. As they ventured into the cave, monsoon flooding rapidly cut off their means of exit. They continued walking further into the cave in the hope of finding a dry, elevated space. They eventually found one, but the route back was completely cut off. Persistent rain in the area also meant that any attempts to rescue them had to wait until the monsoon rains eventually subsided.

The whole world watched the news with bated breath, as a large-scale operation launched to rescue them. Yet incredibly, despite all the odds against them under perilous conditions, a staggering two weeks later, all were found alive and well.

As the frenzied reporters and news media unveiled the first few photos from inside the cave, clear images could be seen of the boys calmly meditating with their football coach, Ekkapol Chantawong. He had trained for 12 years as a Buddhist monk and still meditated daily, so passed on these calming techniques to the boys.

Paul Auerbach of the Department of Emergency Medicine at Stanford University's medical school, who spoke to the Washington

Post about what would have been the boys' mental state at the time said:

> "It's very likely that while the boys were in the cave but not yet discovered by rescuers, they experienced various degrees of anxiety, fear, confusion, vulnerability and dependency, and perhaps hopelessness."[4]

Meditation helped them banish any feelings of negativity or fear that they were not going to escape alive. It was also clear that meditation contributed to them remaining completely calm during the rescue operation, which involved professional divers assisting the boys to dive underwater through the water-logged caves.

Granted, neither you nor I are likely to encounter such a hazardous event in our life, but this true story demonstrates how anxiety can be kept at bay with meditation.

There are other benefits to using meditation as a part of your daily routine. For example, the following show the effect it has on the regions of the brain usually triggered during an anxiety attack.

The Benefits of Meditation

- It regulates the brain so that it stops alerting the amygdala to trigger the fight/flight mode, but instead, triggers the parasympathetic 'calm down' mode.[5&6]

- It reduces the release of the stress hormone cortisol[7]. Too much of this stress hormone wears down the brain's ability to properly communicate fear and anxiety, keeping the brain in a heightened stressed state.

- It exercises and stimulates parts of the brain responsible for emotional behaviour, motivation, awareness and response. It also aids concentration and focus.[8]

- Long-term meditation thickens and strengthens the long stretch of nerves joining the right and left hemisphere of the brain, called the corpus callosum. A thicker corpus callosum means higher intelligence.[9 & 10]

- It improves regions of the brain responsible for learning and memory recall.[11]

Here are scientifically proven reasons why meditation is beneficial to the body overall:

- A study by UCLA found that meditation slows the progression of the HIV virus which causes AIDS. [12]

- Another medical study found that meditation, yoga and support group therapy altered the DNA of breast cancer survivors. The group divided patients into three groups. One was given an eight-week meditation programme with yoga; the second had a 12-week support group therapy with clinical psychologists and social workers; and the third, the control group, had a one-day stress management seminar. The two groups that had meditation with yoga had strong, healthy stretches of DNA compared to those who only had therapy or the one-day stress management seminar.[13]

And finally, meditation has been proven overall to:

- Reduce pain;

- Reduce blood pressure;

- Improve your immune system;

- Increase emotional intelligence and social connection;

- Improve sleep;

- Aid positive emotions and feelings of happiness.

However, as vital as meditation is to your recovery from anxiety, it is just the start.

You still need to get to the root of the problem by changing the way you view challenging situations (for example, think of Brian and his worry about the threat of redundancy). This takes us to the fascinating realm of the subconscious mind which, warrants a chapter of its own, and which follows next.

Summary

The conscious mind is surprisingly limited in its processing capabilities.

You consciously think in a logical, sequential pattern, e.g. "I wonder if I should do this? But what if?" You can only hold one conscious thought at a time. It is a running commentary of what you experience in any given moment, and it all happens in the cortex.

You can however, overcome cortex-based anxiety with:

- Self-inquiry: It helps you take a step back to challenge your thoughts, and view them from a different perspective; secondly,

- Meditation: It helps you to treat unwelcome or obsessive thoughts as if they are noisy cars, bustling along the busy road of your mind, that will soon pass. Using meditation as part of your daily routine regulates (or calms down) regions of the brain usually activated during anxiety. It is also good for your health overall.

The subconscious mind

One would assume that thoughts and emotions are a product of consciousness. After all, you have hundreds if not thousands of thoughts during your every waking moment. However, your thoughts are generated long before you are consciously aware of them, in what scientists call your unconscious mind.[1]

Your unconscious mind is responsible for steering the automatic functions of your body. You do not, for example, consciously think about regulating your heartbeat, when to breathe, when to blink, how to wiggle your fingers, your toes, or how to walk, etc. Your unconscious mind is the processor that takes care of these behind the scenes.

It is also responsible for your deepest emotions, memories, and behaviour. Where you internalise the ideals and belief systems that help you navigate the world around you. One could say your unconscious mind is a storehouse of your character, defining who you are.

Your character, however, is shaped by subconscious influences, what you absorb through your surroundings, the relationships you pursue and the habits you acquire etc. So, one aspect of anxiety that you will need to address is whether you have subconsciously absorbed negative influences.

Now at this point, you have probably noticed that I have switched from using 'unconscious' to 'subconscious'. The term 'unconscious' scientifically refers to the part of the mind we cannot access, which as I explained earlier, is responsible for the automatic functions of your body.

Subconscious, however, refers to the way you collect information in your mind. Specifically, anything that you are not currently focused on. It is a staggering thought that your subconscious mind has soaked up everything throughout your life, without you necessarily being consciously aware of it.

So, because I am interested in the way we are subconsciously influenced by what is around us, I will simply refer to 'subconscious' from now on to avoid any confusion.

As explained earlier, there is a limit to what you can hold in your conscious mind. Anything you do not is filtered to the subconscious. This makes it possible for your mind to handle complex tasks, such as multi-tasking. It probably explains why it is often difficult to focus or concentrate on a challenging task if you are tired.

Have you, for example, experienced temporarily drifting off somewhere while listening to a particularly tedious presentation? Did you find that you could still hear the presenter's voice, but you were not focused enough on what he was saying to be able to recall anything later? The ability to drift in and out between the conscious and subconscious in this way is thought to be a safety mechanism for preventing information overload.

So, how might we be subconsciously influenced by what is around us? Two separate studies give insight into this.

In one study, students were affected by what they read. The test group had to unscramble sentences containing words relating to the elderly: old, grey, retired, etc. On leaving the experiment, the test group were visibly walking much slower than when they walked in – even though they were not consciously aware of their change in gait.[2]

In another experiment, testers ate a meal with fellow participants to test whether companions modify their behaviour on each other's. The experiment showed that when the testers ate more, their companions did too, even though none of the companions noticed adjusting their behaviour.[3]

The experiment went further. At intervals during the experiment and without the knowledge of either the testers or companions, a small weight scale was slipped unobtrusively next to the companions. They immediately modified their behaviour by eating less, regardless of how much the testers ate. Once again, none of them were consciously aware of adjusting their behaviour.

This phenomenon of your surroundings affecting you at a subconscious level, good or bad, is something you experience daily. The aroma of freshly baked bread is comforting and homely; fresh lemon spritzed into a room makes you believe the room is clean; ambient aromas in a shopping mall can persuade you to buy;[4] a woman will find a man more attractive if she sees other women smiling at him (apparently).[5] These are all subtle cues that you act upon, often without realising.

But just because you are subconsciously influenced by your environment, it does not mean you are powerless to simply accept any that might be negative or self-limiting. On the contrary, you can intentionally retrain your thinking to be a positive force for good.

Here is another thought about how decisions drive behaviour. The Max Planck Institute for Human Cognitive and Brain Sciences in Leipzig conducted a study to determine what happens in the brain before a decision is made. Participants had to press a button, either with their left or right hand, and were free to do so whenever they chose. They simply had to remember the time they thought they made up their mind to press the button.

The results of the experiment showed fMRI[6] scanners could detect what participants were going to choose a staggering seven seconds before participants pressed a button. Researchers viewing the images could clearly see activity in the region of the brain responsible for planning.

As neuroscientist and co-author of the study, John-Dylan Haynes said:

"This suggests that the decision is unconsciously prepared ahead of time but the final decision might still be reversible."[7]

How might the final decision be reversible?

I believe it is by reprogramming your subconscious mind.

Reprogramming the subconscious mind

The notion of the subconscious is not a modern-day phenomenon. People have used altered states of consciousness for thousands of years. But it was in the late 19th to early 20th Century that saw pioneering studies into using the subconscious for modern medicine, with what is thought to have been the first form of hypnotism called 'mesmerism' by Franz Mesmer.

This later developed into hypnotherapy by the likes of John Elliotson, James Esdaille, and James Baird. Their evidence-based studies were proof that tapping into the subconscious mind brought biological and physical benefits to the body. The subconscious mind really was capable of 'tricking' the body into healing.

Thanks to scientific research, it is also possible to measure the electrical activity of the brain when it is in a meditative or hypnotic state, to gain an even greater understanding of how beneficial these states are.[8]

During meditation, for example, brain waves are in a reflexive, slow frequency wave called Alpha. When the mind settles in this state, it becomes more focused and powerful, during which beneficial chemicals are released into the body. In 1991 an experiment was conducted by the Biofeedback Institute in which fourteen alcoholics in a state of depression were given alpha and theta wave treatment. After 20 sessions, their depression had been reduced by 80 percent and in a follow-up test 21 months later, they still felt happier.[9]

During hypnosis, brain waves reach an even deeper frequency called Theta. This is where people report relief from stress, pain and afterwards a change in behaviour. For example, we know that hypnosis is extremely successful in helping people stop smoking, lose weight, or overcome dependency on drugs.

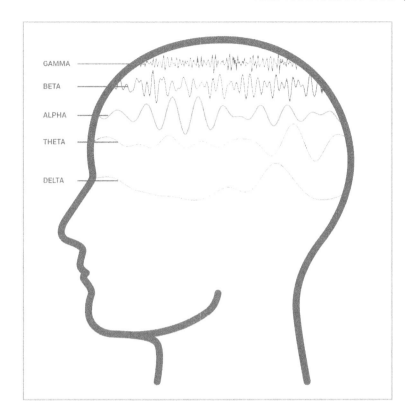

Figure 6: BRAIN WAVES

Free the Mind training taps into both Alpha and Theta states, to fully maximise these benefits for you.

Your subconscious mind is a vat for deeply repressed memories, which is why therapies such as meditation and hypnosis are such useful mediums to control emotional or psychological ailments, and the reason they both underpin Free the Mind training.

Your subconscious mind is waiting to be filled and stored with whatever you choose to fill it, from wherever you choose to fill it. You could think of it as an old-fashioned photographic sensitive plate on which you impress images, beliefs, or ideas.

That sensitive plate does not know the difference between positive or negative, right or wrong. Nor does it matter where those positives or negatives come from. It is just lying there, waiting for you to impress something onto it to process it later. The 'processing' of your sensitive plate happens when your subconscious mind projects those images, beliefs and ideas to your conscious mind, where your decisions are made.

This begs the question: what images, beliefs, or ideas are you impressing upon the sensitive plate of your subconscious mind? If the message you constantly hear in your mind is: "I can't do it", compounded by negative "what-ifs?" you will forever hold yourself back from reaching your true potential.

Your subconscious mind quite literally guides and navigates the decisions you make in life, so you must steer it in the direction you want it to go. If you want to finally end the cycle of negative, self-limiting beliefs, you must proactively steer it in the direction of positive success.

The reason I have focused on how the subconscious mind works, is because your amygdala controls your emotional responses, and your emotional responses are inevitably learned subconsciously.

Can you see just how important it is to reprogram your subconscious mind if you want to overcome amygdala-anxiety for good?

So, how do you programme your subconscious mind?

I recommend a two-fold approach, with firstly self-hypnosis, and then visualisation.

Self-hypnosis

Perhaps when you think of hypnosis, you conjure an image of a smartly dressed man in a waistcoat, swinging a fob-watch before an unwilling participant's eyes, while chanting, "You are getting very sleepy".

While that may have been yesteryear's entertainment for cheap laughs on television, you may be surprised to learn that you enter a state of hypnosis every day when you fall asleep (i.e., the act of falling asleep), when you daydream, when your mind wanders, or when you are focused on something to the exclusion of everything else around you.

Hypnotherapy is simply a means of accessing the subconscious mind when you are in a this relaxed state. But it is not a deep sleep. In fact, research shows that during hypnosis, regions of the brain used for attention, emotional expression, memory and judgement are more active. So, it is in fact a heightened state of focus. By directly accessing these parts of the mind, you could say that hypnosis gets to the very root of the problem you are trying to change.[10]

During hypnotherapy, we use the language that the mind understands best during this state – visual images, metaphor and association. Using this type of language helps your mind to become absorbed in mental imagery or fantasy. This makes hypnosis a powerful tool to reprogram the way you think about things.

A hypnotherapist will use guided imagery to prompt suggestions to a person's subconscious. This will help the person identify underlying issues and then modify their behaviour for desired change – something we call 'suggestion effect' – based on the notion that when the mind is focused on a dominant idea or image, carefully targeted suggestions can elicit a 'reflex'.[11]

For example, if you were in severe pain, a hypnotherapist would guide you to focus on the area of your pain, and by using carefully worded suggestions, would help you imagine the pain disappear.

Or if a person wanted to stop smoking, they may need to tackle associations they have with smoking. Perhaps they usually meet with friends in a social setting and that is when they most fancy having a cigarette. A hypnotherapist would create carefully crafted suggestions to break that association.

But let me dispel one common myth here. No-one can be hypnotised against their will or be made to act as if they are under the control of a hypnotist. Suggestions used in hypnosis are carefully crafted to be positive, in the present, and achievable. They are designed to be evocative. Only imagery that personally means something to the person under hypnosis is used. Hypnosis simply will not work otherwise.

This training simply shows you how to use self-hypnosis, by evoking positive images and suggestions for yourself. To quote Milton Erickson, psychiatrist and psychologist who specialised in hypnosis:

"It is really amazing what people can do. Only they don't know what they can do."

At the age of 17, Erickson contracted a bout of polio which was so severe he fell into a coma. When he awoke three days later, he was paralysed, unable to move anything other than his eyes, and barely able to speak. He still had his mind, however, which he kept active by playing mental games. He also noticed the subtle cues of non-verbal body language, which clearly honed his powers of perception.

He would sit strapped in his chair, seemingly immobile, longing to play outside. One day, while imagining himself playing outside, he noticed the chair begin to rock. This excited him, so he willed himself to walk by giving himself direct commands "move legs", "rock the chair", but nothing happened.

He sank back into his daydreams, again imagining himself playing outside. As before, the chair began to rock. His discovery of indirect suggestion was born. Using this discovery, he taught himself to walk again over the period of two years, aided by closely observing his baby sister who was learning to walk at the time. He was eventually able to walk with the use of a cane. [12&13]

It is an inspiring story, which demonstrates the power of the subconscious mind. But there are many others, such as the story of James Esdaille, a Scottish surgeon who served for 20 years in the East India Company and was well-known for carrying out surgery by what was then called 'mesmeric analgesia,' quite likely hypnosis.[14] The operations are well documented, with patients reported to have not incurred any pain during the procedure.

Or the dental surgeon Victor Rausch who had his gallbladder removed without anaesthetic, drugs or gas, but by simply using self-hypnosis. In his words, the hardest part of the procedure was persuading the surgical team to try his 'insane' idea.[15]

Your feelings, emotions, and thoughts are stored subconsciously. Negative patterns of thinking have stuck through repetition and through not being challenged, at least until now. You will learn how to use self-hypnosis to tap into your subconscious and prepare your mind for change.

Visualisation

We have seen that there are two types of anxiety:

- Amygdala-based anxiety, which is usually emotive: "I feel uncomfortable in this situation, get me out of here", and

- Cortex-based anxiety, which is all thought: "I'm worried about this situation, what if it lands me into trouble, what if I can't find a solution, what if..?"

In either case, the response to the cause of the anxiety is conditioned or learned. You can, however, stop either of the two responses by:

- For amygdala-based anxiety, 'showing' your amygdala (your conscientious little guard) a new way to respond to the situation; and,

- For cortex-based anxiety, reframing your anxious thoughts, and meditating daily.

This is where visualisation becomes such a powerful tool. A picture is worth a thousand words. If it were possible, I would get you to repeat this phrase over again, as it is one of the reasons why visualisation is so useful in overcoming anxiety, with results achieved within a short time frame.

To understand how visualisation works, consider something called Subliminal Messaging, a means of sending visual messages directly to the subconscious, bypassing the conscious mind.

It was first noted in 1957 by James Vicary, a struggling advertising and marketing executive who used a tachistoscope [16] to put short messages lasting 1/30th of a second onto a cinema screen.

He claimed sales of popcorn increased 18% and sales of Coca Cola increased over 50%. Later, in 1962 it was considered a hoax. However, that hoax clearly caused a panic, as it seems to have been enough to cause advertising associations in the US and UK to stop this type of advertising, called sub-visual messaging.

At Utrecht University, a carefully controlled experiment found that if people were familiar with a brand and had a general need, short flashes of a brand even if not seen consciously, would encourage them to buy the product. The subconscious mind was still capable of detecting those flashed images.

Interestingly, the eye does not have to see a complete image. The brain can use subconscious memory to complete the picture. When, for example, Marlborough cigarettes were banned from motor racing advertising, the company used barcoding which if filled in, would resemble the Marlborough logo. The eye saw the barcoding and the brain completed the picture. Clearly, what has already been delivered to the subconscious mind is important, as it in turn feeds the conscious mind with the 'end product'.

But the great thing about visualisation is that you do not have to rely on external imagery. It also works if you use your imagination to conjure the image. Using mental imagery to visualise in this way works for the following reasons:

1. Visualisation requires focus and concentration to perceive the colour, size, shape, or other properties of the image you are trying to visualise.

2. Visualisation has a dramatic effect on the mind and body when you attach emotions to the visualised image. You may not be able to speed up your heartbeat by simply telling it to, but if you visualise yourself swimming away from a great white shark, your heart rate will start racing. Visualisation works best when you infuse a mental image with a dominant, positive feeling so that the scene feels real to you personally.

3. Emotion has a very strong influence on behaviour and happens to be an extremely efficient motivator. Any parent knows that asking their son or daughter to tidy their bedroom will get a far better response if there is a reward at the end of it. The excitement of the reward is the emotion that motivates them to action.

4. Emotion also helps you to remember past experiences more vividly. If I asked you to remember the first time you met your partner, you will quite likely evoke how you felt, while simultaneously recalling any thoughts or images associated with the event. The longer you dwell on those thoughts/images, the stronger the emotion. If, for example, you were to use visualisation to give up smoking, your emotional motivation to stop might be to set a good example for your children. Guided imagery might be of you interacting with them without cigarettes, imagining their pride when you finally give up. Alternatively, for a stronger suggestion, you might be guided with an image of cigarette tar sliding down your throat onto your lungs and coating them with a thick, black, sticky substance. Times 20 if you smoke 20 cigarettes per day. A powerful image to store in your subconscious mind.

5. Finally, research into visualisation shows that when you visualise an action, it stimulates the same regions of the brain that are stimulated when you literally perform the action.[17] An example of this is an interesting experiment which observed a group of

pianists performing a simple one-handed exercise, practising two hours a day for five days. In this experiment, a magnetic 'coil' was placed near the head of the pianists to measure activity in the motor cortex, a region of the brain responsible for the nerve impulses that take care of muscular activity. The results of the experiment showed after a week of practice, the stretch of motor cortex devoted to the pianists' finger movements had considerably increased. Quite literally, more brain space had been used for that specific activity. But the experiment went further. Some pianists held their hands still while only visualising how they would move their fingers. The results of the experiment were extraordinary. Almost identical neural activity was found in the motor cortex area of this second group, compared to the first who physically played.[18]

This shows just how powerful visualisation is as a technique. In fact, it is something high-performance athletes use all the time. Visualisation under hypnosis helped nationally ranked Stanford gymnasts to execute complex tricks they had been working on for over a year.[19]

Imagine being able to visualise a completely new outcome from a situation that would normally cause you anxiety? I can help you with guided imagery, but it will require a complete change in mindset – one I hope you are now ready to embrace.

Summary

Your immune system, bodily functions, emotions, memories and behaviour all operate behind the scenes unconsciously, without conscious thought on your part.

You are however, subconsciously moulded and shaped by many influences – your environment, surroundings, relationships and past experiences. This does not mean you are powerless to simply accept any that might be negative or self-limiting. On the contrary, you can intentionally reverse them.

You reverse subconsciously embedded beliefs by reprogramming your mind with the two-fold approach of:

- **Firstly, self-hypnosis:** You may have developed years of negative patterns of thinking, which have stuck through repetition and by not being challenged. Self-hypnosis allows you to tap into your subconscious, to prepare your mind for change; and

- **Secondly, visualisation:** A picture paints a thousand words. This makes visualisation such a powerful tool for each exercise. Carefully crafted scripts and guided imagery will help you alter the way your mind views situations that would normally cause you anxiety.

SECTION THREE: THE TRAINING PROGRAMME IN DETAIL

Section Three is the crux of the training, where I provide detailed training exercises for the following common challenges in anxiety:

- achieving clarity;

- overcoming self-consciousness and eradicating pre-judgment;

- accepting what you can or cannot control;

- coping with impermanence;

- accepting the concept of failure;

- visualising success; and

- trusting yourself to live and work in the zone.

You will also learn how to get the most out of the exercises, to help you manage your anxiety in any of these situations going forward.

Free the mind training

Reprograming and freeing your mind is only possible if you are crystal clear about your desired outcome. Yes, you may want to be free from anxiety, but why? What, precisely, about your anxiety do you want to change? To stop panic attacks? To stop worrying about things you cannot control? To meet freely in social gatherings? The more specific you are, the easier it will be to focus your thinking on the desired change.

In some cases, old belief systems need to be challenged, reframed and then followed with a commitment to let go. Why not make today the day you decide nothing will stand in the way of you achieving success this time around.

I was crystal clear that I wanted my monkey mind to stop chattering. Up until that point, I was self-conscious, sensing everyone judging me and sizing me up. I often felt uncomfortable in my own skin. I knew recovery was only possible if I believed in the training and completed it each day to lead me to a better place.

In the initial stages of training, I devised strategies to help me move forward whenever negative thoughts entered my mind. I used the image of clear water in a glass to associate it with having a clear mind, and visualised thoughts as clouds drifting peacefully in a clear blue sky. Visualising images like this, is the key to retraining your mind to think differently.

Remember what I referred to earlier, as the photographic sensitive plate of your subconscious mind? Imprint new thoughts and ideas onto it, to help you form new beliefs. Having trained like this for many years, I have every confidence these methods will work for you too.

The basics

The training consists of the following four phases:

- Meditation phase: to put you into a relaxed, meditative state;

- Self-hypnosis phase: to deepen relaxation, and clear your mind to prepare it for change;

- Visualisation phase: which with the use of guided imagery, will enable you to view the challenge differently and visualise a new outcome;

- Exit phase: to help you comfortably return to normal waking state.

The meditation and self-hypnosis phases repeat throughout. The visualisation phases differ, as they have been tailored for each challenge. Each point in this phase should take a minute or two to complete, so it is not something you should rush.

It is very important that your subconscious mind knows why you are doing the training before you start with the visualisation. This is called an affirmation and it makes a big difference to the effectiveness of the training.

For example, you will note that for the exercise on Achieving Clarity, I have suggested your affirmation could be, "I want my conscious and subconscious mind to be as clear as this glass. I want my thoughts to be as clear as the water in this glass."

Your subconscious mind then realises why you are doing the visualisation and will be ready to accept the messages crafted in the visualisation exercise.

Just think of how you may have started your day each morning for the past however many years. You may have woken up, pulled back the curtains perhaps to see the weather outside, and then turned away again to get ready for the day. You may have done this for many years, and it will have had no effect on clearing your ruminating, worrying mind.

Now imagine, pulling back the curtains and saying, "My conscious and subconscious mind is as clear as the glass in this window." You can pause and get ready for the day ahead, while this message of clarity is accepted by your subconscious mind. If you should start a series of negative thoughts or 'what ifs', your subconscious mind will know how to dispel them, or you can visualise the glass as an additional trigger.

The affirmation at the beginning of the visualisation steers your subconscious in the right direction. I have also repeated the affirmation either mid-way or at the end of each exercise, to increase its effectiveness.

In some cases, there are two types of visualisation exercise: "reprogramming" which focuses on longer term reprogramming of the mind, or "emergency calm" which can be used to help you through an immediate challenge, such as to prepare for a forthcoming event.

You should find, however, that after practicing the reprogramming exercise, it may not be necessary to spend as much time on the emergency calm. The purpose of reprogramming is to become conditioned to think differently about a situation altogether, whether performing on stage, delivering a presentation, or attending a social event. I suggest you read through the exercises first to familiarise yourself with them, then select whichever you feel is more appropriate to your needs.

The aim of the first exercise, "Visualising Clarity", is to clear your mind and empty it of thought, as the basis of the training is to help you clear your mind before visualisation.

To help you visualise clarity, have a glass filled with clear water and place the glass on a desk or table next to you before you start the training, so that you do not have to interrupt your flow during the exercise. The glass filled with clear water will help your mind associate clear water with clarity.

The remaining exercises are based on understanding the reality of a situation and reprogramming your mind to view the situation differently.

You might initially find it difficult to remain still and completely quiet, especially if you have a mind that chatters. Be patient and simply refocus on your breathing to deepen relaxation. Alternatively, you may find it helpful to return to the exercise "Visualising Clarity", as it is the perfect primer for your mind to be receptive to change.

You do not have to get any of these exercises right first time around. Return to them as often as you need to, until you become more comfortable with completing them without having to read them.

The visualisation phase of the training is the most powerful of all. The imagery I suggest may at first feel challenging because you are creating new thought patterns in your mind and new neural pathways in your brain. Our brains prefer the easy route of a familiar pathway, one of the reasons why old habits can be difficult to change. Try not to resist the exercise. With practice, it will become a natural process.

You do not have to limit the exercises to visual imagery. Use all your senses. What does the scenario feel or smell like? You need this to be as evocative as possible, so personalise and fully immerse yourself in the experience. Your subconscious mind will store it as a real event.

We know this works in practice because professional golfers use video tutorials to teach someone how to play golf. Once you see a professional demonstrating a correct swing, you can better visualise how to copy the action yourself.

In some of the visualisation exercises, you get to be the star of the show. When I guide you with, for example, imagery of you sitting on a train, evoke as much detail as possible to immerse yourself in it. In other exercises, you will imagine yourself watching the show, such as when I guide you to visualise the delicate balance of nature. It is a different type of visualisation but still works if you create the details. The point is to imagine a good outcome, move on to the next stage, and keep building on each positive outcome.

How to get the most from the training

- Have warm, comfortable clothing in case you become chilly during the self-hypnosis phase.

- Find a safe, comfortable place where you will be undisturbed for at least 15 minutes.

- Sit comfortably in a chair.

- It is easier to create a new habit if you practice it at the same time each day, so try to find a place in your daily routine where you can easily slot this in at the same time. However, this is not a must, just a suggestion.

- If you can, do this first thing in the morning, simply because it is an ideal way to start the day. Once again, this is not a rule. Simply find a time that suits you. It is more important to be consistent.

- Carefully read through each exercise to familiarise yourself with its aims and then practice for at least 15 minutes every day until you feel an improvement in the challenge you want to overcome. When I started training, I was so desperate for a quiet mind, I trained for two 15-minute sessions each day. I suggest you first become accustomed to consistently training for one 15-minute session, until you feel comfortable with the process.

- If you find visualisation easier with imagery, there are image prompts at https://www.freethemindtraining.com. Simply visit the relevant website page detailed in each exercise, and enter the password provided.

- This is where I make one final challenge: will you commit to these exercises daily? An athlete puts in hours of training to beat his or her personal best. A musician practices every day so he or she can play their music without reading the scoresheet. An actor works hard to remember his or her lines. This training is a new habit, so it will take time to become accustomed to it. All it takes is 15 minutes of your time. You WILL have a mind free of anxiety if you stick to the programme each day.

Exercise #1: Achieving Clarity

"If you put a spoonful of salt in a cup of water it tastes very salty. If you put a spoonful of salt in a lake of fresh water the taste is still pure and clear. Peace comes when our hearts are open like the sky, vast as the ocean." Jack Kornfield - The Art of Forgiveness, Loving Kindness, and Peace

Clarity of mind is the ability to see and understand your thoughts clearly. It is the ability to make decisions confidently or work out a variety of strategies to help you arrive at a satisfactory conclusion, even if you do not have the answer immediately in front of you.

Have you ever ventured out in your car during bad weather, and suddenly found yourself in the middle of a snow storm? Lacking mental clarity in life could be likened to driving during that storm with a hazy windscreen. You need to slow down to a snail pace because you cannot see what is up ahead of you.

Similarly, without clarity, you feel confused and mentally foggy, unable to move forward with purpose or intention. Having clarity of mind is equal to having clear vision despite the storm around you. Even if there are hazards ahead, you can see clearly enough to make appropriate decisions, and negotiate your way forward

The aim of this exercise is to help you visualise clarity. It is a short exercise, but extremely powerful, with the association of clear water for clarity of mind. The more often you use this association, the easier it will be for your subconscious mind to accept it.

MEDITATION PHASE

This first phase will help you achieve a relaxed state, clear your mind, and reach a higher level of awareness and inner calm. Remember to place a glass of clear water on a desk or table next to you, within a comfortable line of gaze.

---

1. Begin with your eyes open. Find a place in the room where you can comfortably focus your eyes. You do not have to stare, just be aware of the space around you.

2. Take deep breaths - in through the nose and out through the nose. Focus on expanding your chest and filling it with air.

3. Notice your breaths exhaling but do not try to control your breathing. Just quietly observe it. Allow it to do as it pleases.

4. Close your eyelids, and feel your body becoming heavier until you feel completely relaxed.

5. Become aware of your other senses and whether you notice other sounds around you. You do not have to blot out those sounds. Just be aware of them, and notice them.

6. Inhale counting to 4. Exhale counting to 8. If you can inhale for 6 and exhale for 12, then even better. But start with what you feel more comfortable. Count during the breathing if it helps you to keep focused and relaxed.

7. Feel your body become heavier and deeply relaxed. Feel each muscle softening, like wax melting from a candle.

8. Open your eyes.

9. Concentrate on the clear water in the glass. Gaze at it and nothing else, until your vision starts to dim and the water is all you can see. Allow yourself to feel complete peace and serenity.

Now move onto the self-hypnosis phase to directly access your subconscious mind.

SELF-HYPNOSIS PHASE

The naturally occurring state of self-hypnosis acts as a heightened state of focused concentration. It is deeply relaxing with the added power of helping you directly access the subconscious state of mind to affect desired change.

---

1. Close your eyes. You will now work on ridding your mind of any feelings of anxiety and disquieting thoughts.

2. You might find it difficult to keep a clear mind. If you find that your thoughts keep intruding, don't try to force them away. Simply observe them patiently and allow them to slip away.

3. Count slowly from 1 to 10, then count slowly from 10 back to 1.

4. Repeat to yourself that your eyelids are getting heavier and allow them to slowly close until you cannot keep them open any longer.

5. Instruct your subconscious and unconscious mind to work on having a clear mind by using an affirmation, such as: *"I have a clear mind, free from disquieting thoughts"*. You do not have to use these exact words, but you do need to use positive statements as if you have experienced the desired change. When you instruct your subconscious mind that the change has already happened, that is what it will believe.

6. As in the meditation phase, imagine the tension in your body slowly melting away. Relax your toes, imagine the tension slowly vanishing from them, toe by toe. Imagine the tension

vanishing from your ankles, calves, thighs, hips, stomach, chest, shoulders, neck. Focus on doing this for each part of your body until you feel heavy and completely relaxed.

Now move on to the visualisation phase.

VISUALISATION PHASE - ACHIEVING CLARITY

The following exercise associates a glass of clear water with clarity. When you stop training, your subconscious mind will continue working on the desire for a clear mind. It never stops working, even while you are asleep. You are clearing the subconscious.

Have you noticed that whenever you have a dominant thought throughout the day, your mind is more likely to look for opportunities to fit the dominant thought?

For example, have you ever bought a new car only to find yourself noticing all the other cars exactly like it – the same model, the same year, the same colour? When your mind is focused on one thing, that is precisely what you will notice.

Use the following exercise to create a new dominant thought, mental clarity. This will, in turn, prompt new behaviour.

For imagery, visit *https://freethemindtraining.com/clarity* and enter the password: clarity.

---

1. Start with the following affirmation: *"I want my conscious and subconscious mind to be as clear as this glass. I want my thoughts to be as clear as the water in this glass."*

2. Visualise a clear glass on your shoulders. Imagine that it is half filled with clear water.

3. Imagine that this glass of clear water replaces your head. The glass represents your subconscious mind. The clear water

represents past thoughts and experiences, but everything is totally clear.

4. Any negative thoughts that may come into your mind cannot penetrate this glass or discolour the clarity of the water.

5. Now, visualise a clear blue sky on a summer's day. If you have negative thoughts, picture them as clouds that occasionally appear in the sky. Do not dwell on them, simply allow them to gently pass by, so that you are eventually left with a clear blue sky again.

6. Your clear mind is as endless as the sky is deep. You now know that if you have any intrusive thoughts, they will simply float by just like clouds.

7. Take this even deeper by visualising your mind as clear as a lake. It is so clear you can see the sand, rocks or grass on the lake floor.

8. Repeat the affirmation, *"My mind is as clear as this glass. My thoughts are as clear as the water in this glass."* Remember, the aim is to completely clear your mind.

9. Bring yourself slowly back to conscious awareness. Tell yourself, *"I am fully awake and alert. My mind is clear."* Take your time to orientate yourself internally before opening your eyes. You may want to visualise yourself entering a room and opening the door before you open your eyes.

HOW TO APPLY THIS GOING FORWARD

A clear mind is one that is still, calm, and free from disturbance.

Have you ever seen a small pond, perhaps at the bottom of a garden, with a surface so calm and still you can see the reflection of the surrounding trees, the sky and the clouds reflected on it too?

Use the visualisation exercise to practice seeing your mind as calm as that pond. When thoughts come and go – perhaps like ripples on the pond disturbing its stillness – simply allow those ripples to settle. Take the visualisation further by imagining the water is so clear, you can see the bottom of the river bed.

This exercise is tantamount to clearing away the clutter of negative, self-limiting thoughts that may have built up over the years. Once the clutter is gone, you can begin the exciting next step of planning what you really want in life. New goals, new beginnings.

Do remember that you are influenced by what surrounds you. So, why not start by clearing a special space for your new mind training routine. Remove any physical clutter from your space so that the concept of freeness, space and clarity surrounds you.

Begin to think more carefully about the people you surround yourself with. You may want to start seeking out new local groups, or online forums where people gather to inspire and motivate each other.

Remember, the mind training games referred to earlier which lead to better memory recall? A quick search online will reap a host of fun games you can play – either online or as an App on your smart phone. These will keep you alert and focused, and will do wonders for your concentration going forward.

Make this visualisation a daily habit – preferably first thing in the morning – and like a good breakfast, you will find that it sets you up for the day ahead.

You will have clearer thought, clearer decisions, less rumination, less worry, and ultimately less anxiety.

Exercise# 2: Overcoming Self-Consciousness and Eradicating Pre-judgement

"People are crying up the rich and variegated plumage of the peacock, and he is himself blushing at the sight of his ugly feet." Saadi

Your self-esteem is vital for a sense of self-worth. It is the extent to which you value your ideas, opinions, beliefs and image. Simply put, whether you like yourself.

However, as anxiety causes a warped view of self, you may find it difficult to like yourself or even perceive yourself in a true light. So, if we take for example, the thought "I've never been good at math," in anxiety, it becomes "I've never been good at math, and I never will be."

Remember, your subconscious stores whatever you impress upon it, projecting those ideas to your conscious mind for you to act upon. The risk of leaving self-limiting thoughts unchecked is that you can become socially disconnected.

Here is an example of someone, who we will call 'Graham', who has social anxiety:

'Graham' avoids social gatherings, because he hates the idea of someone staring at him or waiting for him to introduce himself. He worries people will think he is stupid, that his voice will quiver, that he will sound afraid and will come across as awkward. Ironically, because this is how he feels, this is how he acts and comes across to others.

He also suffers from profuse sweating, which makes him feel more embarrassed. Graham feels he has no control over social situations so prefers to stay away

from them wherever possible. This makes him feel isolated, which worsens his
anxiety further.

The root of what is happening in this scenario, is that Graham has a conditioned response to what he (falsely) believes others are thinking. He then associates this belief with the unpleasant experience of sweating and panic. The result is that each time he has these 'offending' thoughts, his response is the same.

If you have thoughts like Graham's, remember (a) you do not have to believe them, you can challenge and reframe them; and (b) you can permanently reprogram your mind to think differently altogether.

Another aspect of self-esteem is feeling overly self-conscious, taking your shortcomings and obsessing over them to the point where you feel you cannot move forward because of them.

Imagine if your inner critique was the type of person who jabs you on the arm, while they criticise everything you say or do. You would want to get as far away from them as possible.

But aside from the critical self-talk, when you get to the root of what self-consciousness is, it is imagining what other people think about you. Reflect on that for a moment. Not only are you worrying about something imagined (not necessarily true), you are worrying about other people's thoughts. There is a limit to what you can control, and other people's thoughts are one of them.

Use the first exercise to help you put your thoughts about yourself or what you perceive others think of you, into context. The second exercise is designed to help you challenge pre-judgements. We all form opinions in our mind, often based on first appearances, but these judgements are rarely based on fact until we get to know someone better.

1. Start with the meditation phase.

2. Move on to the self-hypnosis phase.

3. Now move on to the visualisation phase.

VISUALISATION PHASE: OVERCOMING SELF-CONSCIOUSNESS

Take your time to immerse yourself in this exercise, as opposed to just reading it. This will impress on your subconscious mind the reprogramming that we are trying to achieve. For imagery, visit: *https://freethemindtraining.com/overcoming-self-consciousness/* and enter the password: overcome-self-consciousness

---

1. Start with the following affirmation: *"My conscious and subconscious mind know that I am one person in a vast world full of many different people living in towns, cities, countries and continents."*

2. Visualise a national stadium full of people, perhaps a football or rugby match. Its roof, pitch, and stand.

3. Visualise somebody in the crowd. Zoom out and picture another, and the person next to them. They look different to you but place your name inside them. It is as if this person is you.

4. Come out further, picture another supporter. Keep going until you notice the steward, tag your name onto them. The person in the ticket office, the policeman/policewoman, the train driver and further out. Of all the cars along the route to the stadium, picture someone inside and tag your name.

5. Travel to another country: China. Place your name and person into a worker in a vast textile factory. They are all lined up in rows working on the sewing machines. Tag your name onto this worker, imagine this is you.

6. Imagine yourself in New York City, as someone going to work on the subway. To India and a lady preparing her family for school. She is in a cramped building on a busy street in the city. See how she is dressed, she looks totally different to you; tag your name onto this person.

7. You are in Australia, where it is now night but a doctor is working a shift in the hospital. Picture clearly the doctor in his or her scrubs, different in appearance to you but tag your name as if it is you.

8. Visualise yourself in Germany where a man is holding a business conference. He is just about to walk into the conference hall with a name tag on his jacket. It has your name, but his appearance is totally different; visualise this person.

9. Place your name into a young girl in a classroom in Brazil. Picture the girl and the scene and tag your name. Place your being in a farm worker in Ethiopia.

10. Always range further out and see the accompanying people at the same time. Pick a port, a city, a village. You are one person in a vast world who could be living in any country.

11. Now picture yourself in a shopping mall, at school, in a business forum, in a plane, in a restaurant and zoom out and see all the other people. Do you know them well? Do they know you?

12. You are just one person among millions. How does this make you feel? There are so many people in the world, 7 billion. You are only one amongst many. You are unlikely to remember people in a crowd, so why should they notice you?

13. Repeat your affirmation: *"My conscious and subconscious mind know that I am one person in a vast world full of many different people living in towns, cities, countries and continents."*

14. Bring yourself slowly back to conscious awareness. Tell yourself, *"I am fully awake and alert. My mind is clear."* Take your time to orientate yourself internally before opening your eyes.

VISUALISATION FOR EMERGENCY CALM: ERADICATING PRE-JUDGEMENT

For imagery, visit *https://freethemindtraining.com/eradicating-pre-judgement/* and enter the password: eradicate-pre-judgement

---

1. Start with the following affirmation: *"I see the physical form of a person, but I don't know their character or background so can't make a correct judgement."*

2. Picture yourself on a train. It is crowded, perhaps during rush hour. Take in all the different people. Some are smartly dressed, others casually dressed.

3. You overhear someone talking, they have a well-spoken voice. You notice someone else is rough in appearance. Create whatever details you would like. Take in all the sights and sounds.

4. What first opinions do you have of these people? Your thoughts have no bearing on their character. You do not know them, so your opinions are not based on fact.

5. You see a man with tattoos all over his arms, chatting to a girl who has piercings in her ears, through her nose and on her lips. Your first impression of them is that they are uneducated, from a difficult inner-city background.

6. You see a lady wearing a smart suit, reading through some notes taken from her briefcase. She is sitting next to a man with earphones looking at his phone. You assume she is well brought up, an over-achiever, perhaps a lawyer in a city firm.

You consider the man to be a mature student, working on a PhD but probably not working hard enough to pass his exams.

7. You notice a man with dirty, tattered clothing, sleeping on a barrier within the train. You think he must be sleeping rough. In your mind, he has had a hard night and is probably going out begging to save money for his next drink.

8. Picture a young lady wearing jogging bottoms and a lycra top. She picks up her water and gets ready to leave the train. You immediately think that she is yet another over-achiever, but this time, the type who is only interested in getting to the next 'big thing'.

9. Are any of these assumptions true? What if, you misjudged them all?

10. The man and girl with the tattoos are friends from Oxford University. They both went to a top private school and are now working in the technology sector. The lady in the smart suit was brought up in an inner-city council estate. Her background was surrounded by drugs and gangs with knives. She has worked hard to put herself through college, has worked her way up through the company and is now a personal assistant to the CEO.

11. The man with the earphones is relaxing before starting a long shift, working on the floor of the London metal exchange. He has some big positions and wants to take his mind of work. The man in tattered clothing is a top lawyer who has finished an Outward Bounds course. He is exhausted and is going home to rest. The young lady dressed in lycra is heading to the gym before acting on stage at the national theatre.

12. Your initial pre-judgements of these people were wrong. And they will also have preconceived ideas of you, most likely incorrect, based purely on what they see.

13. Imagine any one of these people looking at you, smiling at you. They do not know you. They might be forming an opinion of you. What is it? You could imagine they think badly of you, but equally, you could imagine they think well of you. First impressions – good or bad – are based on pure conjecture, until we get to know someone properly.

14. Repeat your affirmation, *"I see the physical form of a person, but I don't know their character or background so can't make a correct judgement."* Visualise your disquieting thoughts disappear.

15. Bring yourself slowly back to conscious awareness by stepping down from the train onto the platform. Perhaps you sit quietly on a bench until the train passes, quietly observing all the interesting characters you have just witnessed as the train disappears into the distance. They are gone. Do not be concerned what people think of you. We have no control over pre-judgements.

16. Take your time to reflect on how happy this new understanding makes you feel.

17. Slowly orientate yourself internally before opening your eyes. You may want to visualise yourself walking through the station's exit and slowing entering your home again, opening the door before opening your eyes.

18. Tell yourself, *"I am fully awake and alert. My mind is clear."* This will help your mind return to a fully conscious state.

HOW TO APPLY THIS GOING FORWARD

The key to living a happy, self-fulfilled life is to feel comfortable in your own skin, and that requires a healthy, balanced view of yourself.

You may have become so used to feeling anxious, that you now view the world around you negatively. Perhaps each day is spent psyching yourself up for things to potentially go wrong – queuing in a supermarket, travelling on public transport, walking down a busy road – tasks that everyone else takes for granted, for you may seem insurmountable challenges. This is taking a 'better to be safe than sorry' coping mechanism, and it is not going to serve you well in life going forward.

One experiment took 28 patients with generalised anxiety disorder (GAD) and 16 people with no history of anxiety, to test how they judged challenges

All were first trained to identify three slightly different tones of sound (300, 500 and 700hz), and each of those tones were associated with a decision. One tone would gain them money, one would lose them money, and one would lead to nothing. All they had to do was press a button if they recognised any of the original tones.

The results found that people with GAD consistently chose the tones that represented a loss, compared to people who had no anxiety who simply chose what they heard. In other words, anxiety had negatively altered the perception of the anxiety sufferers to the extent that they were predicting a worst-case scenario.[1]

Think about that for a moment. If you go through life predicting a worst-case scenario, it means you must either create a safety net around you to cushion the effects of that scenario, or alternatively, avoid the scenario altogether.

Through such a negative viewpoint, the world becomes a seemingly dangerous, hazardous place that you must dodge or navigate around, which of course leads to more anxiety.

The thought, "When I go for a walk, everyone stares at me," leads to the thought, "When I go for a walk, everyone stares at me, so I'd better stay at home. I'll be safer here."

But now that you have experienced the visualisation exercises on self-esteem and challenging pre-judgement, why not flip the thought on its head to, "When I go for a walk, it's quite likely no-one will even notice me." Or even better still, "When I go for a walk, someone might notice me. But hey! Who cares!"

It will take practice to believe the "who cares" part of that thought, but I promise you, with practice, you will achieve it.

To partly quote C.S. Lewis:

"What you see and what you hear depends a great deal on where you are standing." The Magician's Nephew.

Perception is imagined. If you are walking along a narrow country path and suddenly come across a boulder, is the boulder an obstacle or a handy stepping stone? The answer is purely down to perspective. If you view the boulder as an obstacle, a hinderance blocking your path, at best it is a frustrating bothersome thing, at worst it has ruined your journey. If you view it is a handy stepping stone, it has become a useful tool to propel you forward.

The power of perspective is that you get to change how things appear and the affect they have on you. Use these visualisation exercises to reframe how you think or feel about yourself. Do not be concerned with what others think about you (or to be more precise, what you imagine others think about you). We have no control over other people's thoughts or their pre-judgements.

You now have the power to create a new script. What will you write differently? What will you do differently? Make new friends? Have an engaging conversation with someone at a party? Have fewer ruminating thoughts?

Visualise yourself in control of the new situation, of you calmly walking up to someone with a pleasant smile on your face and initiating an interesting conversation. This takes practice. But remember, you can change the way you feel about anything. You are in control.

In Stephen R. Covey's acclaimed best-seller, 'The 7 Habits of Highly Effective People', he outlines seven approaches to attaining personal goals. The second habit is 'begin with the end in mind'. In other words, decide where it is you want to be, compared to where you are now, then work towards your goal.

What is your ideal result? If you want to be more confident, what are you wearing as this confident person? How are you standing? Who are you with? Just as an example, how many people before they get married think about what their ideal partner or spouse would be like?

The ONS has revealed that in the UK, 42% of marriages end in divorce.[2] Admittedly there are many factors that contribute to divorce and people can, of course, change. However, how much thought do people put into the character and personality of their best suited partner before meeting them? You need to know the goal before starting the expedition. The more you visualise the result, the more real it will seem to you right now.

Exercise #3: Letting Go Of Control

"You have the power over your mind, not outside events. Realize this and you will find strength." Marcus Aurelius

Control is a good thing. When you have it, you feel stable, safe, balanced, and comforted. Being in control means you are ready for what comes next. When you can anticipate the outcome, you can be suitably posed for action. A certain level of control is even good for your health, as people who feel more in control of their lives reportedly have less aches, pains, and faster recovery from illness.[1]

However, anxiety can present a warped sense of control – i.e., a fear of losing control, leading to obsessively trying to hang on to it at all costs. Here is an example to illustrate:

'Teresa' has obsessive compulsions around safety. On waking, she checks that light switches around the home are turned off, despite turning them off the night before. Locks on windows and doors are checked to see whether they are secure. In the kitchen, each appliance must be checked for signs of damage. Oven and hob knobs are checked to ensure they are turned off, knives or other sharp objects must be safely tucked away. On leaving home, she locks the front door, yet returns twice to see if it is still secure. Teresa feels temporary relief when she is carrying out her safety checks, but as soon as she is away from the home, she feels on edge as she cannot be entirely sure she has covered everything. She often spends the rest of the day mentally retracing her steps, worried that she may have put her family in danger because of her neglect.

There are three aspects to Teresa's anxiety:

- Obsessive thoughts: "If I don't switch off the oven or hob, there could be a fire".

- Compulsive behaviour: Thoughts precede actions, so the seemingly logical action after the thought, "If I don't do this... " is to do it.

- Temporary relief: Teresa's temporary relief from carrying out her safety checks deceives her into thinking she has control over the situation. However, when obsessive thoughts return, the cycle begins again.

If thoughts like Teresa's are causing you anxiety, be assured that you can regulate them, by:

1. Firstly, meditation which will allow your thoughts to flow and eventually pass (much like the cars in the illustration of the busy road referred to earlier).

2. Secondly, self-hypnosis which will enable a deeper state of relaxation to prepare your mind for change.

3. Thirdly, with the suggested imagery in the visualisation exercises, change the way you view the issue of control altogether. This will provide long-lasting relief instead of the fleeting temporary relief usually achieved between cycles.

The following exercises will help you feel you can safely let go of control where appropriate. Read them first, then once you become familiar with each concept, feel free to change the imagery to personalise them.

1. Start with the meditation phase.

2. Move on to the self-hypnosis phase.

3. Now move on to the visualisation phase.

VISUALISATION PHASE FOR REPROGRAMING: ACCEPT WHAT YOU CANNOT CONTROL (A)

For imagery, visit *https://freethemindtraining.com/control-part-a* and enter the password: control-a

---

1. Start with the affirmation: *"I have no control over outside events."*

2. Visualise yourself preparing for an important interview. Create as much detail as possible. See yourself researching the organisation, preparing brilliant answers to tough interview questions. Then journeying to the office, entering the imposing building and finally, seated in the reception area waiting for your interviewer to arrive.

3. Visualise the interview. Yourself sitting opposite the interviewer with him or her quizzing you about your knowledge, experience, skills, or suitability for the job. Think of the effort it has taken you to perform this interview at your very best.

4. Now switch your focus to a week, perhaps two weeks, later. The postman has slipped a crisp, white envelope through your letter box. It falls gently on the floor in front of you. You instinctively know this is the response you have been waiting for.

5. Visualise yourself gently prising open envelope and removing the letter - just enough for you to scan the first few lines.

6. You quickly see the words, "We regret to inform you…" Notice how you feel. Disappointed? Angry? Upset? Whatever the feeling, do not avoid it. Embrace it. Is it in the pit of your stomach? In your throat? Hold it. Feel it. Understand what it is, then allow the feeling to pass. However long it takes, it will pass. It is only a feeling.

7. You had no control over who the interviewer decided to choose for the role. The job may have already been taken internally or given to the son or daughter of a senior employee within the company. The interviewer was looking for a certain person for the job, a certain skillset, a certain academic background. You sadly did not fit the role. Allow the reality of this scenario to sink in. Is there really anything you could have done to change the situation? Perhaps you could have performed better in the interview. But how much control did you really have over the situation?

8. Repeat your affirmation: "I have no control over outside events."

9. Take your time to orientate yourself internally before opening your eyes. You may want to visualise yourself entering a room and opening the door before you open your eyes. Tell yourself, *"I am fully awake and alert. My mind is clear,"* to help your mind return to a fully conscious state.

ALTERNATIVE VISUALISATION PHASE FOR REPROGRAMING: ACCEPT WHAT YOU CANNOT CONTROL (B)

For imagery, visit *https://freethemindtraining.com/control-part-b* and enter the password: control-b

---

Visualise any of the following alternative scenarios:

1. Start with the affirmation: *"I know that fate will play a role."*

2. You are on your way to an important meeting. You are smartly dressed, ready to meet colleagues and associates. You arrive at the station early, but your train is delayed for 45 minutes. This was the only train that would have got you to your meeting on time. Notice how you feel. Disappointed? Angry? Upset? Recognise it. Notice how it feels. Then as before, allow it to pass. It is only a feeling. The train was late. There was nothing you could have done to prevent this from happening. You have no control over this situation.

3. Visualise yourself competing in sport. You were given a bad refereeing decision. You have no control over this decision.

4. See yourself on a City financial markets trading floor. You have taken a significant risk, like a gambler who has bet on a horse. Suddenly a huge dramatic event affects market trading. The markets move wildly and your trading position changes dramatically. You have no control over this situation.

5. An unexpected election result causes a change in government, affecting business. You have no control over the decision.

6. Imagine you are a farmer. See yourself next to a field full of crops. Suddenly overnight, there are violent storms and torrents of rainfall. Visualise the field, now flooded, the crops destroyed. Zoom out, the storm and flood have devastated a community. You have no control over this situation.

7. Visualise yourself as a baby, the hospital ward you were born, the city, the town. Now visualise yourself in any of these scenarios:

    a. in a small village in India

    b. in a busy, overpopulated city of Lagos in Nigeria

    c. in a small village of Nomads in Africa

    d. in a tiny hospital in the snow-covered grounds of Tibet.

8. Visualise the life you would lead in any of these scenarios. There is no control over where you were born, in which social group you find yourself or who your parents are. Any one of these could have been your environment.

9. If you are in a relationship, think back to how you met. Was it by chance? Of all the places you could have gone that day, it just so happened that you met your partner. How much control did you have over the situation?

10. As before, repeat your affirmation: *"I know that fate will play a role."*

11. Take your time to orientate yourself internally before opening your eyes. You may want to visualise yourself entering a room and opening the door before you open your eyes. Tell yourself,

"I am fully awake and alert. My mind is clear," to help your mind return to a fully conscious state.

VISUALISATION FOR EMERGENCY CALM: LEARN TO LET GO OF CONTROL

For imagery, visit *https://freethemindtraining.com/let-go-of-control* and enter the password: let-go-of-control

---

1. Start with the affirmation, *"I am going to be free from anxiety and fear."*

2. Imagine you can turn whatever it is that is troubling you into an object, e.g. a scrunched-up ball of paper. Visualise yourself taking it, screwing it up, scrunching it smaller and smaller with as much enthusiasm and intensity as you can muster.

3. Now visualise yourself carefully placing it into a bag and taking it with you into the woods.

4. It is a pleasant day, warm but perhaps slightly breezy. You feel both the warmth of the sun and the breeze across your cheeks. You can hear the birds chirping in the trees above you.

5. You continue walking deeper into the woods, until you reach a river. You carefully reach into your bag and take your small, scrunched-up ball of trouble. Visualise yourself taking it out and tossing it into the river. You hear the gentle splash of the water as it hits the lake.

6. Tell yourself, *"I give myself permission to let you go. I am free from worry and anxiety."* Repeat this affirmation or something similar, visualising your fear around control disappearing.

7. Stand and watch it as it drifts slowly downstream, the gentle tide taking it further and further away. Watch as it slowly drifts and then slowly sinks, until eventually, it disappears completely beneath the water.

8. Do not take your eyes off it. Watch it as it disappears, then say *"goodbye"*. How do you feel? Pleasantly relieved?

9. You hear the birds continue to sing, the sun is still warm and the breeze is still cool on your cheeks. You turn to come back home again.

10. Bring yourself back by slowly walking back through the woods, this time taking in everything around you. You are pleased to come back home, anxiety-free and ready to start a clear new day.

11. As before, take your time to orientate yourself internally before opening your eyes. You may want to visualise yourself entering a room and opening the door before you open your eyes. Tell yourself, *"I am fully awake and alert. My mind is clear."* This will help your mind return to a fully conscious and clear state.

HOW TO APPLY THIS GOING FORWARD

In sports, there are bad refereeing decisions. A dramatic event on the global scene affects market trading. A change in political government affects business. A drought affects farming. A major storm, flood or other form of natural disaster can devastate a community. These are events that no-one can control.

Bring this concept a little closer to home and you realise you cannot completely control your own life. Not entirely. Exam results, sports performance, your health. You can work hard, study hard, practice more, eat healthier etc., to achieve a desired result, but you cannot literally control the results. All you can control is your reaction to them.

I was recently diagnosed with tinnitus. Interestingly, when I was first diagnosed, I regarded it as a nuisance having had perfect hearing all my life. It took me a little while to reflect on the fact that had I previously been partially deaf but could now hear with tinnitus, I would be overjoyed at having gained some hearing. That slight shift in viewpoint has helped me to accept my new lot in life and plan a way forward.

When you reflect on the uncertainty of the world around you, you realise there is freedom in not trying to predict or control the outcome of everything. After all, trying to predict the outcome of everything is tantamount to predicting the future – and who can reliably do that?

Give yourself permission to let go of control, and simply focus on what you can do right NOW.

Exercise # 4: Accepting Impermanence

"Do not be afraid of death; be afraid of an unlived life. You do not
have to live forever, you just have to live."
Natalie Babbitt, Tuck Everlasting

A topic not often discussed, at least not in the West, is the reality of physical impermanence. Perhaps it is a failing on our part, that we do not talk about the loss of a loved one, and possibly one of the reasons bereavement can cause extreme or prolonged anxiety. In cultures where it is accepted or even embraced, people seem to have a less morbid attitude towards it.

When a loved one passes away, we struggle to come to terms with why. However, one way to cope with loss is to seek comfort in nature. When we observe nature, we realise despite the delicate balance of life that fades and withers away, there is mostly life.

I often take a walk along a river near my home, where I notice the ducks wading. Sometimes mother duck has as many as ten ducklings, scurrying behind her to keep up. When I return a few weeks later, I notice she has only four ducklings left. Yet you can tell by her occasionally swimming back to gather them closer if they paddle off again, that she is no less attentive for having lost the six. She is still an attentive, loving mother duck.

The following exercises are designed to associate nature's gentle reminders of change, with the reality of impermanence. I have used the stages of a butterfly, and the seeds of flowers that germinate, grow, wither, then fade. Equally, you could use the foliage of trees changing from buds in Spring to bare branches in Winter.

There is change all around us and we are part of this transformation.

1. Start with the meditation phase.

2. Move on to the self-hypnosis phase.

3. Now move on to the visualisation phases.

VISUALISATION FOR REPROGRAMING: ACCEPTING LOSS

For imagery, visit *https://freethemindtraining.com/accept-loss* and enter the password: accept-loss

---

1. We are not going to visualise death. This must be strictly observed. We are simply going to show the subconscious mind images of the cycle of life up to and including old age.

2. Start with the affirmation, *"I can keep growing and developing within the passage of time."*

3. Visualise the life cycle of a flower. A seed sitting on the rich, brown soil. At times, the seed is soaked with rain, at other times, it is warmed by the sun.

4. Germination eventually begins, and as the hydrated enzymes within the seed develop, its metabolic rate increases. Roots soon appear from the bottom of the seed; the stem protrudes and starts to develop. The plant begins to grow.

5. Visualise its growth from a small seed to a fully-grown plant with leaves.

6. Now see its buds appear on each shoot, slowly opening and turn into richly-coloured beautiful flowers.

7. These bright coloured flowers now attract a bee, brushing the anthers within the flower as the pollen grains attach themselves to the bee. It flies to another plant, where the stigma attracts the pollen grains from the bee, resulting in pollination.

8. The pollen grain starts to grow. The nucleus of the pollen grain passes down the tube in the flower and joins with the nucleus of the ovule - fertilisation.

9. The seed is blown, taken away from the flower and deposited on the ground.

10. The old plant now begins to change colour and wither. It droops, and slowly looks less healthy.

11. Other seeds begin to germinate, and the cycle starts again.

12. Tell yourself, *"I am fully awake and alert. My mind is clear."* to help your mind return to a fully conscious state.

ALTERNATIVE VISUALISATION FOR EMERGENCY CALM: THE CIRCLE OF LIFE

For imagery, visit *https://freethemindtraining.com/circle-of-life* and enter the password: circle-of-life

1. Start with the following affirmation: *"We are all part of the cycle of life."*

2. Visualise yourself being able to closely observe the life of a butterfly. Zoom in closer to the leaves it has laid its milky white egg that will become a Monarch butterfly.

3. Look closer still and imagine you can see its metamorphosis. The egg slowly bulging, expanding, morphing into a tiny caterpillar.

4. Closer still until you can see the tiny caterpillar munching on the juicy green leaf. See the caterpillar slowly yet steadily munching its way around the leaf until it finally has no choice but to adjust itself to wriggle onto yet another leaf.

5. You now notice the caterpillar becoming fatter, longer and larger until its skin becomes too small, and that it falls swiftly to the ground below. You watch as the caterpillar grows new skin and moults again – at least four or five times more.

6. Visualise the caterpillar, adjusting itself again until it hangs upside down. See its skin split and wrapping itself in a pale, green chrysalis.

7. You notice the chrysalis becoming paler, until it becomes transparent. You can see inside. The chubby, striped caterpillar has transformed into a beautiful black butterfly with striking yellow stripes on its wings.

8. You see the legs, abdomen and head come out of the chrysalis first. Yet it does not let go of the branch, as its wings are not quite ready.

9. Its abdomen is swollen, full of fluid ready to be pumped to its wings to allow it to fly. The butterfly rests on the branch, waiting for its moment to fly.

10. When it does, it flies towards you and very briefly rests on your nose, as if to thank you for watching, and flies away. You follow her as she flits from flower to flower, leaf to leaf until she finally finds a mate.

11. Her flight is laboured and within weeks she will wither. But you notice the milky white eggs she has left behind.

12. You can use the following, or similar, affirmation at this stage, *"We are all part of the cycle of life. I accept my journey to old age. But I am grateful for this present moment of beauty."* This prepares your subconscious mind that you will inevitably lose loved ones.

13. Bring yourself slowly back to conscious awareness in a way that feels most comfortable to you and slowly orientate yourself internally before opening your eyes. Tell yourself, *"I am fully awake and alert. My mind is clear",* to help your mind return to a fully conscious state.

ALTERNATIVE VISUALISATION FOR EMERGENCY CALM: FIND COMFORT AFTER LOSS

For imagery, visit *https://freethemindtraining.com/comfort-after-loss* and enter the password: comfort-after-loss

1. Visualise an image of a peaceful place - perhaps your garden, a favourite park or a favourite room in the house.

2. Take in all the details of this favourite place. It is where you feel at peace. It is comforting, quiet and no one can disturb you.

3. From now on, this is a quiet 'retreat'. Start with the affirmation, *"I can enjoy my haven of peace."*

4. What do you see yourself doing in this place? Reading? Passing the time away with a favourite activity?

5. There is no one here to judge or criticise you. You are alone to completely relax and release the tension of holding in your emotions. Allow yourself to fully experience them, then allow yourself to release them slowly at your own pace, and whenever you feel ready.

6. You can say another affirmation at this point if you wish: *"I choose to heal myself. I am not going to hold back. I allow myself to be fully here."*

7. You can come here whenever your emotions become difficult to bear. With practice, in time, you will heal.

8. Bring yourself slowly back to conscious awareness in a way that feels most comfortable to you and slowly orientate yourself internally before opening your eyes.

9. Tell yourself, *"I am fully awake and alert. My mind is clear"*, to help your mind return to a fully conscious state.

HOW TO APPLY THIS GOING FORWARD

It is important to state here that grief is a perfectly natural process to help you survive the devastation of loss. Health professionals have identified five common stages:

1. Shock and Denial: Initial difficulty in coming to terms with the loss.

2. Anger: As the reality of the loss sinks in, feelings of anger or frustration at what has happened may occur. This anger may even be directed towards the loved one, for leaving the bereaved behind to bear the loss.

3. Guilt: Feelings of what could have been done to prevent the loss – "If only" or "What if" – which may be accompanied by feelings of guilt that something could have been done differently.

4. Anxiety or Depression: It is only natural for sadness to set in as the loss of a loved one begins to influence the bereaved person's life. This stage may also see a change in diet or sleep.

5. Acceptance: The final stage when the bereaved person comes to accept the reality of the loss and learn how to adjust to a new life without their loved one.

These are not linear stages, as if each of them should be experienced before or after the other. They may come in sweeps and waves or they overlap each other. Each person's process will differ.

Neither is there a length of time that it takes to grieve. So never feel as if you should be over your loss 'by now', or that you should simply learn to pull yourself together. Do be assured, however, that you can get through to the other side. You may, for example, find some comfort in the following case study of one of my clients, who I will call "Sue".

'Sue' came to see me to discuss her bereavement. She had lost a daughter aged 33 and then her son aged 27 shortly after. Her husband died a few years later.

Her daughter had owned a hairdressing salon at the end of the road. She had enjoyed many visits to the salon, chatting with her daughter and clients, before going on to work night shifts as a nurse. But after the death of her daughter, the salon had been sold and turned into a convenience store. Not only had she lost three members of her family, she had lost the means of seeing friendly, familiar faces.

She revealed that even before her loss, she tended to worry and often felt agitated. By the time she came to me, her mind churned from one negative thought to another. She was, understandably distraught, on edge and could not get past feeling a complete loss of control over the events in her life. She was in such a bad state that she would constantly call the doctor, and on one occasion called for an ambulance in the middle of the night.

She had a barrage of thoughts: "Why had this happened to her?" "What could she have done to prevent the death of her loved ones?" "Could the hospital have done more?" "Could she continue without them?" "Why had she not treasured the moments more when they were alive?" "Did they know how much she loved them?" She had tried to use reason or logic to get past these thoughts but could not find peace.

She felt physically ill, nervous and lacked the confidence she once had. She was having regular panic attacks and at times, agoraphobia. The smallest of tasks felt burdensome, which she said, was in stark contrast to the busy life she previously had of looking after a family of four. She was desperate for help.

I knew the mental training would help her, but I was concerned she would not feel settled enough to even try. I asked her to carefully consider whether she was prepared to put in the training for 15-30 minutes each day. She came back later in the day, determined to be taught the techniques.

We started by concentrating on clearing the mind, to stop the cycle of self-reflection and rumination. To help focus her mind, I had her count 60 breaths, count in for 6 seconds, then exhale for 12.

We moved onto the exercise "Visualising Clarity", with her imagining her mind as clear as the glass of clear water in front of her. I encouraged her to not dwell on intrusive thoughts, to not get angry at any inability to focus on the water and glass, and to understand this was merely the start of a training programme that would get better with practice. We worked through this together, with her focusing on clarity. At times, we imagined her mind as an endless blue sky, with thoughts as passing clouds. She would lock on to this image of clarity, managing to do so even while looking through a window observing people bustling along outside. I would occasionally have to nudge her back into focus, as her attention span was limited due to distracting thoughts. But she made incredible progress each time she visited. It was not long – within a few days – that she had much better focus and concentration.

Sue progressed until she felt ready to tackle the subject of impermanence. It was important that she felt comfortable to do this at her pace. I wanted her to give herself permission to believe that her husband, son, and daughter had known all along that they were much loved and treasured. They would have wanted her to move on with a happy, fulfilling life, while keeping them treasured in her memory.

We started by visualising the life of a lion, born a cub, growing into a young lion, then accepted and settled into a pride. In time, the lion would give birth, look after its young, hunt for food and then reach full maturity.

We then visualised the life of a flower. Seeds dropped onto the fertile ground, germinating, the plant growing, its flowers blooming in full display. We saw the bees buzzing around the flowers, flying away with tiny pollen sacs stuck to their legs, dropping those sacs and pollinating more seeds to grow elsewhere.

We worked through this a few more times, then briefly visualised (but did not dwell) on positive moments loved ones can have during a lifetime. A first date, a first job, cherished moments and family holidays. It was important for us to associate impermanence with acceptance, love and fond memories - not morbid fear, guilt and dread. We rounded off the training with sessions on her perception of fate and destiny, finalising with exercises on helping her feel less self-conscious.

The results were astounding. Gone was the edgy nervous Sue who started the programme just two weeks before. She was calm, confident and looking forward to moving on with her life.

Sue told me that one day, her youngest daughter noticed a glass filled with clear water on the kitchen table and was about to take it away to be washed-up when Sue stopped her, telling her to put it back. They both laughed as Sue explained it was part of her training, and that no one should stop her routine. The perfect student!

She now has a clear mind, free from the chronic anxiety she used to suffer. Gone are the constant negative thoughts that used to invade her mind. No more phone calls to the doctor or hospital, no more panic attacks, and no more agoraphobia. She has an active life outdoors, busy volunteering at her local church, being involved in charitable events, various clubs, shopping, visiting friends, and finds solace in visiting her local cemetery once a week.

Exercise # 5: Challenging A Fear Of Failure

"Success is not final, failure is not fatal: it is the courage to
continue that counts." Sir Winston Churchill.

No-one enjoys failing. Just think, from the moment you attend junior school, you learn you must obtain the best grade or else risk the disapproval of your parents, teachers or fellow students.

Occasionally, merits are awarded for taking part, but they often seem to be awarded reluctantly. Even where subtleties to exam passes are introduced – sliding scales, percentiles and suchlike – the significance of failure is not lost on either student or parent. They still know what constitutes an A* or A. By the time a young man or woman leaves university, it will have been thoroughly drilled into them that success in life depends on a first-class pass. It is not uncommon for students to feel a 'failure' for only achieving a so-called measly second.

Of course, no one sets out to fail, but rarely are we taught that failure is a constant in life and a stepping stone to success. The money-broking world of the 90s was full of people who had barely passed an exam. But they were extremely hungry to win the trade. They knew their clients were their bread and butter. They would fight for each deal.

"Develop success from failures. Discouragement and failure are two of the surest stepping stones to success." - Dale Carnegie.

I have often seen children at tennis tournaments being severely criticised and scolded by their parents for losing a match. The blame game begins, and the child soon learns to fear failure by either fleeing situations, or not competing at all. The child then develops anxiety over disappointing their parents, resulting in them unable to compete enthusiastically.

"Fear is only as deep as the mind allows." - Japanese Proverb.

Use the visualisation exercise to help you accept the reality of failure.

1. Start with the meditation phase.

2. Move on to the self-hypnosis phase.

3. Now move on to the visualisation phase.

VISUALISATION PHASE FOR REPROGRAMING: ACCEPTING THE CONCEPT OF FAILURE

For imagery, visit *https://freethemindtraining.com/do-not-fear-failure* and enter the password: do-not-fear-failure

---

1. Start with the following affirmation: *"Nature fails all around me, I can learn from defeat and then progress."*

2. Visualise a cheetah hunting for food. See it furtively creeping in the long grass to catch a gazelle. It stops and watches its prey, ready for the attack. Have this picture in your mind. The gazelle looks up but sees nothing, then carries on eating the grass. All seems still, but now is the time for the attack.

3. Visualise the cheetah burst into full speed running towards its prey. The gazelle looks up and immediately darts off to safety. The cheetah chases after the gazelle, but just as she is ready to pounce, the gazelle darts left and then right. The chase goes on for a few minutes until the cheetah, running out of energy begins to slow.

4. One final effort. The cheetah chases again, but on this occasion, the gazelle is more agile. The cheetah stops, defeated, having failed to get her food. The gazelle slows down and stops. Peace has returned and the gazelle is left alone, eating the grass again. The animal kingdom is full of failure. Why should life for us be any different?

5. Visualise an eagle perched on a rock in a mountainous region, scouring the plateau below to find some food. She sees something moving down below that looks like a small rabbit.

See the eagle take off, looking intently at the land below. She sees the rabbit and hovers above, waiting for the time to pounce and grab her prey. The rabbit senses danger and runs to hide.

6. Picture the eagle swooping down, but just as it is about to grab its prey with its claws, the rabbit disappears down a small burrow. Picture the eagle pulling out of the dive, just missing the grass and slowly climbing back up to perching again on its rock. The eagle has failed, no food was collected on this attack. The bird kingdom is full of failure.

7. Now picture a farmer planting seed in his field. See the crops beginning to grow and soon after, a field full of rich corn, wheat or barley. However, a storm rages, lasting for many days and nights. Picture the scene as the wind and rain batter the crops. A field once full of life and abundance has now been destroyed, flooded with water. Visualise the scene of devastation as the crops are now lying on the ground, ruined, not available for harvest. The life of a farmer is often fraught with these failures, why should we be any different?

8. See a large vineyard full of grapes, ready for picking. A freak drop in temperature has resulted in a heavy frost. Grapes are ruined, with most fallen to the ground now useless. Others are still on the stem but will be without taste.

9. Repeat your affirmation: *"Nature fails all around me, I can learn from defeat and then progress."* We must accept failure can happen to us. We can try but cannot guarantee success.

10. Tell yourself, *"I am fully awake and alert. My mind is clear"*, to help your mind return to a fully conscious state.

HOW TO APPLY THIS GOING FORWARD

A study of high school and university students[1] found that fear of failure can be divided into two camps. In one camp are over-strivers, students who will do anything not to fail. While this may seem like a positive, they find setbacks hard to accept, a weakness. There is also the implication that if a setback feels impossible to overcome, it can lead to depression.

The second camp are fear avoiders, students who feel uncertain about their abilities and have a heightened sense of self-doubt regarding their personal success. While they are hard workers, they are adversely affected by setbacks as 'confirmation' of their self-doubt. This type will use self-sabotage or delay tactics such as procrastination, to give an excuse for not doing well, e.g. "I failed because I did not have enough time to complete it", rather than face failure due to a lack of ability.

Perhaps this is cultural. I often hear children in the U.K. boast that they have not revised. It is considered cool to NOT work hard. In Japan, this attitude is unheard of. Everyone, from child to adult, takes work seriously. The flip side is that they seem to be more risk-averse than their peers in other countries. In a 2014 report from the Global Entrepreneurship Monitor, less than one in three working-age adults in Japan considered starting a company a 'smart career' choice.[2]

Or perhaps it is an indictment of our celebrity-mad culture, which presents a skewed reality. The media portrays the world as sprinkled with a large dose of fairy dust. Perfectly muscular men in perfectly toned bodies, alongside beautiful women in a perfect sized zero. When you spend too much time with these false ideals, you risk setting yourself up for a spectacular disappointment.

The reality is that we are all flawed, and everyone makes mistakes. Even the world's most successful leaders have had fails:

- On the night of 14th of April 1912, the Titanic received no less than six warnings of icebergs ahead, but she was travelling near her maximum speed by the time her lookouts sighted them. Unable to turn quickly enough, the ship suffered a glancing blow that buckled her starboard side and opened five of her sixteen compartments to the sea. The sinking of the Titanic is, to date, the worst disaster at sea in history.

- In 1962, the record company Decca chose a band called 'Brian Poole and the Tremolos' instead of 4 men from Liverpool. 'The Beatles'.

- Seated in Palo Alto's Mandarin Gourmet restaurant in March 1998, Larry Page and Sergey Brin prepared to pitch Paul Flaherty, a Stanford Ph.D. and an architect of AltaVista, on the merits of their superior search engine technology. They hoped AltaVista would pay as much as $1 million to get access to the soon-to-be-patented PageRank system. Page and Brin would then be able to resume their studies at Stanford. With the help of Stanford professors and the Office of Technology Licensing, Brin and Page tried unsuccessfully to sell their 'Google PageRank' system to Excite and other search engines. In 2018, Google was valued an estimated market net worth of $800bn.[3]

- In the summer of 2009, Facebook turned down Brian Acton for a job. Brian later met Jan Koum at Yahoo, where they both worked. They formed a partnership and soon left Yahoo to become co-founders of the messaging service WhatsApp. Facebook acquired WhatsApp in 2014 for $19bn.[4 &5]

- The late Steve Jobs, who started Apple in his garage with partners Steve Wozniak and Ronald Wayne, was fired from the very company he began. Apple was valued in 2018 an estimated net worth of $1 trillion.[6]

- Walt Disney dropped out of school at an early age in a failed attempt to join the army. One of his earlier ventures, Laugh-o-Gram Studios, went bankrupt due to his lack of ability to run a successful business. He was once fired from a Missouri newspaper for "not being creative enough", yet his movies have brought joy to millions of young and young at heart ever since.

- J.K. Rowling was rejected by scores of publishers, famously posting two of the rejection letters on Twitter to encourage aspiring authors.[7] When asked how she kept motivated in those early days, she said, "I had nothing to lose and sometimes that makes you brave enough to try."

- Michael Jordan, whose remarkable achievements make him the greatest basketball player of all time, famously said: "I've missed more than 9,000 shots in my career. I've lost almost 300 games. Twenty-six times I've been trusted to take the game-winning shot and missed. I've failed over and over and over again in my life. And that is why I succeed."

- The inventor Thomas Edison said: "Negative results are just what I want. They're just as valuable to me as positive results. I can never find the thing that does the job best until I find the ones that do not." He should know. He had many unsuccessful inventions before he perfected the commercially practical light bulb.

- The aviation industry spends millions of dollars investigating air safety, deliberately crashing planes to learn vital lessons on airline and passenger safety.[8]

The above examples and plenty more like them, show just how important failure is as a precursor to success. Rather than fear failure, embrace it to keep you learning and moving forward.

Exercise #6: Challenging A Fear Of Success

"Nothing in life is to be feared, it is only to be understood. Now is the time to understand more, so that we may fear less." Marie Curie

Related to the fear of failure is a fear of success. If you are persistently shielding yourself from making mistakes, then you are clearly preventing yourself from the prospect of success.

A colleague of mine had this to say about the prospect of teaching both failure and success to her son.

"It is interesting watching my son being taught rugby, aged 10. It is a competitive sport, yet the Rugby Football Union have declared that this year, there can't be any declared winners or losers because the children are too young. They score the matches in tournaments, yet no winners' medals can be given anymore. Everyone gets a medal for taking part instead.

I have competitive children who want to win, and as a parent I want competitive sport to be about aiming to win yet coping with 'failure' if you do not. There are many lessons to be learned here, yet I now have a frustrated son who, on the one hand can't celebrate what might be a win, and on the other hand can't learn from what might be a loss. My personal view is that this is not setting him up well for real life, and perhaps shows a generational shift in attitude towards failure."

I agree. We should not fear failure, but neither should we fear success in the false belief that success might offend. When I look back on my money-broking days, it would have been laughable for any one of us to not put effort into winning a deal, in case one of our colleagues wanted to get there first. We all knew what we had to do to succeed.

I remember desperately trying for months to create a relationship with a top trader based in Europe. My attempts to get through to him were often met by his secretary uttering the words, "He's busy."

One day, I succeeded in getting through, and he invited me to dinner. Towards the end of the meal, he announced that he would answer my calls if I could answer one question correctly out of the eight he posed. I got them all wrong – not exactly a successful start.

I returned to London feeling the evening had been great fun, but sensed I had not achieved the result I hoped for. Two months later, I got an instruction to give him a call. The conversation lasted less than 10 seconds. "Where do you see the price of this structure?" he asked. He clearly liked what I had to say. "Get me the offer and I'll buy $250m," was his response. The trade was completed, and a great relationship began. Perhaps messing up those eight questions was not the end of the world after all.

A happy, healthy mind accepts there is a balance between occasionally getting things wrong and occasionally getting things right, while revelling in the opportunity to learn along the way.

Use the following visualisation exercise to visualise success. It is carefully scripted to leave you feeling empowered and ready to take on a challenge. Use it when you feel anxious about stepping outside your comfort zone. And while we are on the topic of comfort zones, remember that your comfort zone is precisely that. Yours. Resist the urge to compare yourself to friends, family or colleagues, as if you should be able to cope simply because they can. Take it at your own pace.

1. Start with the meditation phase.

2. Move on to the self-hypnosis phase.

3. Now move on to the visualisation phase.

VISUALISATION PHASE FOR EMERGENCY CALM: VISUALISE SUCCESS

I have created a script you can use for giving a presentation, but you can change the details to suit any scenario. Create as much detail as you can: the shape and size of the room, the colour of the walls, the tables, chairs, people who are there, etc. The more detail you visualise, the easier it will be for your subconscious to accept it as a new reality.

For imagery, visit *https://freethemindtraining.com/visualise-success* and enter the password: visualise-success

---

1. Start with an affirmation, *"A positive mind will influence a beneficial outcome."*

2. Visualise you entering a conference room, about to give a presentation. Take in all the details of this room and everyone in it.

3. You notice your audience smiling in eager anticipation. Their hands are poised, ready to welcome you with a round of applause because they admire you. They know you are an excellent speaker, the best they have heard on the topic you are about to present.

4. Take in their smiles, the look of admiration on their faces, the round of applause, their eager anticipation. It feels good. It fuels you, pumps you full of energy, propels you forward.

5. Your smile becomes a chuckle and then a laugh. Giddy excitement. Hold that feeling and continue walking, confidently, slowly up to the podium.

148

6. You arrange your notes and quickly glance down at the topics you will present. You are now ready to share your knowledge. You take a sip from the glass of still, clear water next to you. You open with a humorous anecdote. The audience laughs, and you begin your presentation. Every phrase is confident, well-rehearsed and on point. You do not rush. You are calm, your breathing is slow and rhythmic.

7. You intersperse your speech with humour, illustrations, and more anecdotes. Just what your audience loves to hear. They get the point, you make it so well.

8. You conclude to rapturous applause. You love this part. It feels completely natural. You genuinely like these people in front of you, and they genuinely like you too.

9. You step down from the podium and spend time milling with the audience, answering questions, shaking hands, exchanging business cards.

10. Hold on to the feelings you have had throughout your presentation. The confidence, the calmness, the exhilaration, the excitement, the pride of sharing your knowledge. These feelings are entirely appropriate and well-deserved.

11. As you leave the conference room, you reflect on the speech and look forward to giving another one. Your affirmation at this point is, *"I believe in myself. I confidently met this challenge and I can confidently meet any challenge. It feels a natural part of my life."*

12. Congratulate yourself on giving such a great presentation and bring yourself safely back to awareness in a way that feels most comfortable to you.

13. Slowly orientate yourself internally before opening your eyes. Tell yourself, *"I am fully awake and alert. My mind is clear"*, to help your mind return to a fully conscious and clear state.

HOW TO APPLY THIS GOING FORWARD

You have a unique opportunity to visualise success, whatever that means to you personally. The brain's response to a visualised image is on par with experiencing the scenario in real life, so practice seeing success and feeling it. Create a new lifestyle that is no longer held back by your anxiety.

Napoleon Hill would visualise meetings with the people he most admired. His practice was originally designed to, in his words, "impress my subconscious mind through the principle of auto-suggestion, with certain characteristics I desired to acquire." His imaginary 'investors' in his visualised meetings would 'speak back' to him giving great insight.[1]

The exercise can help you do something similar. If you usually have anxiety in social gatherings and you have a forthcoming event to attend, use the exercise to rehearse how you will confidently enter the room with a smile on your face and head held high.

If it helps you to imagine you are someone whom you admire and look up to, then that is perfectly fine. Take in their physical details and attributes. Why do you admire them? Is it the way they speak calmly and confidently? The way they make eye contact with the person they are speaking to? Is it in their handshake that is firm, warm, strong and welcoming? Do they have a hearty laugh?

The more detail you can add to your visualisation, the more your subconscious mind will welcome it. This is your opportunity to plot out and practice your game plan, something professional athletes do all the time.

Exercise #7: Trust Your Body
You Can Live and Work In The Zone

"I am never wrong when it comes to my own possibilities."
Placido Domingo

Professional athletes know they must trust themselves to perform at their peak. They cannot afford to second-guess their next move. They know they must act promptly, instinctively and smoothly with synchronicity.

But you do not have to be a top performance athlete to benefit from the same principle. You have spent considerable time reading up on the concept of training your mind to keep it in peak performance and in the zone. You now know that you can reprogramme your mind and trust it to do its job for you.

But in case you need one final reminder, here is further scientific proof that you really can trust both mind and body to do its job:

- Your body is made up of 7 octillion atoms[1] and you are made of 37.2 trillion cells.[2] If your mind has the power to heal your body (remember the placebo effect), how powerful does that make your mind?

- Neurons in your cerebral cortex will be with you your entire life. Remember, the incredible power of your brain to adapt due to neuroplasticity. You now have strategies you can use to reprogramme your cortex for the rest of your life.

- There are a trillion nerves powering your memory. Remember, thoughts are impressed on the 'photographic sensitive plate' of your subconscious mind, and thoughts precede action. Be careful what you feed your subconscious.

- Your eyes can distinguish between 2.3 and 7.5 million distinct colours. Your eyes soak up a lot of detail and the mind loves imagery. Use your mind's 'eye' to create as much detail as possible during your visualisation exercises.

- Your nose can differentiate between 1 trillion different smells. Use your sense of smell during the exercises too. The imagery will feel more believable if you imagine the fragrance or aroma of the scene.

- Your heart beats 100,000 times per day, pumping 5.5 litres of blood per minute. This amounts to 3 million litres a year. Meditation activates the parasympathetic nervous system, which lowers your heart rate, improves blood flow, enhances digestion and slower breathing – all beneficial for your body overall.

- If you put all the DNA molecules in your body end to end, the DNA would reach from the Earth to the Sun and back over 600 times (100 trillion times six feet, divided by 92 million miles). Yet DNA is a fragile molecule that can be damaged, leading to diseases such as cancer. Remember the study referred to earlier, that meditation, yoga and support group therapy altered DNA?[3] Incorporate meditation as part of your daily routine and you will be proactively doing all you can to improve your physical health overall.

Apply the strategies and exercises you have learned, practice them regularly going forward, and trust your body to do its job. Allow it to act instinctively on your behalf, because if you put in the training, it will.

Not trusting in it having got this far in the training, would be like Usain Bolt stopping mid-way through a 100m race, to check whether he is as far ahead in the lead as he thinks he is. Hold that image for a moment! Watch him in action as he hurtles towards the finish line, and you can tell he has absolutely no doubt in his mind that he WILL win.

With this training, you can win too.

The aim of the following exercise is to dispel any fears you may have regarding your ability to change, or that you are beyond help. Now that you have put so much effort into re-programming your mind, trust it to serve you better. This exercise is a way of showing appreciation to your body for the marvel that it is.

1. Start with the meditation phase.

2. Move on to the self-hypnosis phase.

3. Now move on to the visualisation phase.

VISUALISATION PHASE FOR REPROGRAMING: TRUST YOUR BODY

For imagery, visit *https://freethemindtraining.com/trust-your-body* and enter the password: trust-your-body

---

1. Start with the following affirmation: *"My body and mind have great power to achieve. I can trust myself to be in the zone."*

2. All the parts of your body are interrelated to achieve an amazing 'machine'. Visualise each part, from toe to head and feel that they are relaxed.

3. First see your toes, feet then legs. Up through your legs to the fulcrum of the knee. How these are pivotal for walking. Visualise your powerful thigh muscles and hamstrings.

4. Travel up to your stomach. Visualise inside and see the workings of your digestive tract, the 30-foot-long muscular 'tube' that breaks down your food and drink into smaller molecules of nutrients. See how your blood absorbs these nutrients and carries them throughout your body for cells to use for energy, growth, and repair.

5. See your ribs protecting your heart and lungs; appreciate the workings of each; the vitality of your blood coursing around your body.

6. See your skeleton, its solid bones, all 200 of them. Your 600 muscles with amazing ligaments, tendons and joint tissue holding everything together to keep you the incredibly flexible, moving machine that you are. Your skin, your body's

first line of defence against invasion of bacteria and harmful environmental toxins.

7. Travel higher towards your neck, throat, mouth, its passageway for food and drink, vital fuel for your body.

8. Your nose, how its sense of smell enriches the world around you. Your ears and the many sounds you can detect even in just one moment during the day. Your eyes and its different parts enabling you to see – how light passes through the cornea; the iris regulating the size of your pupils; the lens that focuses light onto the retina; how visual information travels as electrical 'signals' through the optic nerve and millions of nerve fibres to the brain so that you can 'see' the image in your brain.

9. And finally, your brain, which you have read extensively about. Now you can visualise its millions of cells and electrical impulses firing back and forth, stimulated by Free the Mind training, and adapting to new thought experiences.

10. You are an amazing form. Repeat your affirmation, *"My body and mind have great power to achieve. I can trust myself to be in the zone."*

11. Bring yourself safely back to awareness in a way that feels most comfortable to you and slowly orientate yourself internally before opening your eyes.

12. Tell yourself, *"I am fully awake and alert. My mind is clear,"* to help your mind return to a fully conscious state.

HOW TO APPLY THIS GOING FORWARD

You have heard that a healthy mind equals a healthy body. Equally, it can also be said that a healthy body helps a healthy mind.

Have you noticed there is a link between what you eat and your mood? This could be down to the enteric nervous system (ENS), located in the sheaths of tissue that line the oesophagus, stomach, small intestine and colon. It is so complex, scientists nickname it the body's 'second brain'.[4]

The ENS is in fact, a network of neurons (100 million of them), built into your digestive system. Food digestion requires a variety of precise chemical mixtures, produced at the right time and delivered to the right location.

The way the ENS seems to do this, is by using chemical detectors to identify chemicals in the food you eat. This 'data' then helps the ENS enlist the appropriate digestive enzymes to break down your food into particles your body can absorb. It is as if the ENS has its own reflexes and senses to control your gut.

Scientists now believe the ENS carries information to the brain, and that a large part of your emotions are influenced by the nerves in your gut. Hence the expression 'butterflies in my stomach' when you are nervous. This could be the ENS diverting blood away from the stomach when the brain experiences stress.

That voice in your head begging for a snack might not be coming from your mind, but your gut sending transmitters to your brain.[5] It does this by influencing serotonin in the brain, an important chemical for regulating happiness.

So, feed your brain with the type of food it needs to stay happy and healthy – a diet that is energy- and nutrient-rich – this will contribute to you having a clearer, healthier mind.

Here are just some examples of what that means in practice:

- You get a steady supply of energy to the brain through glucose in the blood. To sustain a steady supply of energy, eat low-GI goods, which release glucose slowly into the bloodstream. This will keep you mentally alert through the day.

- Your brain needs essential fatty acids and omega 3-fats, which naturally occur in nuts, seeds, and oily fish such as sardines, mackerel, herring and kippers. Omega 3-fats also help to keep your mood stable.

- Blueberries have the highest number of antioxidants, which are linked to a reversal in memory loss.[6]

- Tomatoes contain lycopene, a powerful antioxidant that could protect against the type of free radical damage to cells which occurs in the development of Alzheimer's and dementia.

- B6, B12 and folic acid, found in eggs and green leafy vegetables, help to reduce a compound called homocysteine, which is linked to stroke and cognitive impairment.[7]

- Vitamin C, found in citrus fruits, improves mental agility.

- Broccoli is high in glucosinolates, a compound which slows the breakdown of acetylcholine, which we need for the central nervous system to perform properly;[8] and finally,

- Vitamin E, found in nuts, helps to prevent cognitive decline, particularly in the elderly.[9]

And the following is what happens if, conversely, you do not have a healthy diet:

- Sugar acts like a drug by activating dopamine levels, the neurotransmitter responsible for the reward and motivation system in the brain. When you reach for a slice of rich, dark, double-chocolate cake and tell yourself you deserve another slice, you have triggered dopamine, which in turn triggers more chocolate craving. The occasional craving will not do any harm, but regular cravings will create constant highs. The more you eat, the more you crave. The problem with too much sugar is that it ages brain cells, which can lead to type 1 or type 2 diabetes. [10]

- High fat in the diet has been linked to structural brain defects. [11]

- Research shows evidence of a relationship between unhealthy dietary patterns and poorer mental health in children and adolescents. [12]

The above is a poignant reminder that you are what you eat. It also highlights the importance of maintaining a healthy diet for optimum health, quite literally from the head down.

I have always been an active person and now swim every day to maintain strength in my upper back. But frankly, even something as simple as a daily brisk walk will help you keep fit and improve your mood.

Walking releases endorphins in your brain to keep you in a happy state. It also happens to be the easiest and most readily available of all forms of exercise. It needs very little in the way of clothing or equipment – just a pair of comfortable shoes – and it costs nothing. Why not factor it into your day from now on.

Here are seven reasons why walking is so worthwhile.[13]

- It reduces the risk of cardiovascular disease by 11%.

- A brisk walk helps to decrease BMI.

- It lowers blood pressure and increases aerobic capacity (your body's ability to transport and use oxygen during exercise) by up to 19%.

- It lowers levels of the fat that can cause hardening and narrowing of your arteries (triglycerides).

- It increases your good cholesterol.

- It increases muscle endurance.

- It leads to longer life (one study showed that walking at least two hours a week reduced the risk of premature death from cardiovascular disease by about 50%).

- Experts say that a moderate stroll for 30 minutes (at 3.21km/2m ph) can burn 100 calories, or a much brisker walk if you can manage it (6.4km/4m ph) can burn 155 calories.[14]

All it takes is 30 minutes each day of moderate exercise to stay reasonably fit and healthy. There is even an App which monitors how far you are walking, called Moves, downloadable from the iPhone or Google App Store.

Equally as important to diet and exercise is sleep, which is linked to improving your mood. Make bedtime a ritual and do something soothing, such as read or listen to music to help get you into sleep mode.

CONCLUSION - BRINGING IT ALL TOGETHER

You now have a superb toolbox of new tools and resources to both understand and overcome your anxiety. You can now move forward to live a blissfully happy, self-fulfilled life, free from the crippling effects of chronic anxiety.

By way of summary, here is a recap of the main points I have covered in the book.

Understanding fear and anxiety – the basics

There is a difference between fear and anxiety. Fear is a direct response to literal danger, whereas anxiety is a fear-conditioned response which leads to internal conflict.

Both fear and anxiety trigger the fight/flight response. However, in anxiety, the response is inappropriate and if left unchecked, can lead to stress, depression or chronic health problems.

There are usually two pathways to anxiety:

- **Amygdala-based:**   You feel anxious long before you understand why;

- **Cortex-based:** Slower and thought-based, triggered by obsessive thoughts, distressing thoughts/images or rumination.

Understanding these two pathways means that you can use the appropriate strategy for overcoming either type of anxiety.

Overcoming anxiety – why train the mind

Managing anxiety begins with managing thoughts, which of course, begin in the mind.

Your mind and brain operate in a symbiotic relationship. Your brain, in all its power and capability, can be stimulated by your mind through acquired knowledge, abstract learning and meditation. Equally, your mind clearly benefits from a strengthened, stimulated brain.

Use the full width and breadth of your mind to reprogram the way you view situations or events that would normally cause you anxiety:

- **The conscious mind and cortex-based anxiety**: The conscious mind is surprisingly shallow, the tip of the figurative iceberg. Your immediate conscious thoughts are a logical, running commentary of what you are experiencing in any given moment and it is all cortex-based. This is where 'what-ifs' and rumination occurs. Thoughts precede actions. Learn how to reframe your thoughts so that you change the way you react to situations that would normally cause you anxiety. You can also overcome cortex-based anxiety by making meditation a regular part of your routine. It allows you to observe worrying thoughts in a different light, allowing them to pass by (much like the traffic in our noisy road illustration). Meditation also regulates regions of the brain normally affected during anxiety.

- **The subconscious mind and amygdala-based anxiety:** You are subconsciously influenced by past experiences, your environment and/or surroundings. Your subconscious mind is the 'photographic sensitive plate' upon which you impress messages (whether positive or negative, good or bad). It merely accepts whatever you impress upon it, to then create decisions for you to consciously act upon. Feed your subconscious mind with positive messages from now on.

You can overcome amygdala-based anxiety with the threefold approach of the training by:

(i)   making meditation a regular part of your routine for the reasons explained above;

(ii)   self-hypnosis which deeply relaxes the mind and prepares it for change;

(iii)   visualisation to change the way your mind views challenging situations. A picture paints a thousand words. The mind loves imagery, which makes visualisation such a powerful technique to complete the training.

Summary of Exercises

1. **Achieving Clarity (pgs.100-101):** Press the 'pause button' on rumination or worry, the negative running commentary of 'what

ifs'. Visualise the clear glass of water to help your subconscious mind associate it with true clarity of mind.

2. **Overcoming Self-Consciousness and Eradicating Pre-judgement (pgs.108-113):** Put your thoughts about yourself into context. Remember, you do not have to believe negative, self-limiting thoughts. You can reframe them. Additionally, any thoughts you have formed about what you think are other people's thoughts, are not necessarily based on fact. The world is a huge place with billions of people who are extremely busy with their own cares. The aim is to have a mind that can switch off and not be full of pointless negatives.

3. **Accept What You Cannot Control/Learn to Let Go of Control (pgs.119-125):** Control is a good thing. When you have it, you feel stable, safe, balanced, and comforted. However, use these exercises to help you accept there is a limit to what you can reasonably control, and that you can safely let go of control where appropriate.

4. **Accepting Impermanence (pgs.129-134):** These exercises are carefully scripted to associate nature's gentle reminders of change with the reality of impermanence. There is change all around us and we are part of this transformation.

5. **Accept the Concept of Failure (pgs.140-141):** No one sets out to fail, and neither should you. But allow yourself to accept that you cannot avoid it altogether. Just as importantly, it is a vital stepping stone to success.

6. **Visualise Success (pgs.148-150):** You have a unique opportunity to visualise success, whatever that means to you personally. The brain's response to a visualised image is on par with experiencing the scenario in real life, so practice seeing success and fully

embracing it. Create a new lifestyle that is no longer held back by your anxiety.

7. **Live and Work in the Zone (pgs.155-156)**: You have spent considerable time learning how to train your mind, to keep it in peak performance and in the zone. You now know that the training exercises will reprogramme your mind for good. Trust both mind and body to do its job.

WHAT NEXT?

The future of anxiety treatment

Mental health professionals and scientific experts specialising in anxiety indicate that the future for anxiety treatment is exciting.

On the one hand, scientists hope to be able to use biomarkers.[1] This refers to changes in the body's normal state (such decreased levels of protein, or hormonal imbalances, etc.) to help professionals understand how best to treat diagnosed mental illnesses and 'tailor' appropriate medication.

On the other hand and of interest to me personally, is the cognitive behavioural approach. There is evidence to suggest that anxiety disorders share common elements.[2] So, instead of trying to find specific treatments for each individual anxiety disorder,[3] professionals are calling for a transdiagnostic approach to treat the common underlying factors of anxiety. [4]

In other words, look at why anxiety occurs, not just treat the symptoms. This makes sense, as after all, if you do not understand why you have anxiety, you cannot effectively come up with strategies to overcome it. This is the approach I have tried to take with Free the Mind.

A footballer might be at home on the pitch playing in front of tens of thousands of supporters and millions of television viewers yet struggle to be alone. We all react to anxiety in different ways, however we all have the capacity to reprogram our mind.

Mind training – A long-term solution

My final few words of encouragement are to not give up before you have given this a fair chance. You may for example, wonder why the need to train and not just read the book?

You must reprogram your mind to think differently about the cause of your anxiety. I remember worrying about the smallest of things that would, in the scheme of things, make very little difference. The more I tried to stop worrying, the worse it would get until it snowballed into a full-blown anxiety attack. I desperately wanted a mind that was calm, one that did not jump from one worrying thought to the next.

Once I realised this mind training really worked, I understood I had to persevere. Just as an athlete must learn new habits and practice them to perfect their game, you too will greatly benefit from regularly practicing this training to change what may have been years of an anxious mindset.

The training will not seem easy first time around, because you are after all forming a new habit. But please do not write yourself off as a failure. Very few people can command the mind to be quiet at the click of a finger. You do, however, have help in the form of the step-by-step instructions within the scripts. Keep practicing them until each exercise has been learned by heart. You will soon find that you can run through the exercises without having to read them.

You may have fears around self-hypnosis, for example, that you will not be in control. Be assured that you always have complete control – only you have control of your mind.

Or perhaps your fears are around self-hypnosis not working for you. It can if you are willing to try. It does require concentration to self-induce hypnosis, but you will still have your full faculties, so it is not like sleep. The best way to describe it is the state you are in when you are lost in a great story. You are so engrossed, you do not notice anything or anyone else around you, until you hear the tail end of a conversation: *".... did you hear what I just said? You weren't listening at all, were you?"*

And finally, remember a picture is worth a thousand words. Visualisation is the most powerful tool of the programme, as you can use it to visualise your desired change. You may find it challenging at first to conjure images, but as with meditation and self-hypnosis, it simply takes practice, so be patient.

If your mind begins to wander, allow it to wander and then gently bring it back again. It is probably easier if you do not force the mind to create images. Instead, think of the visualisation scripts I have provided as idea prompts. The more you reflect on the ideas, the easier it will be to train.

What are the benefits of sticking with Free the Mind training?

- you will overcome the cycle of chronic anxiety, chronic worry, rumination and panic attacks;

- you will reduce stress (which can lead to heart attacks, hypertension, chronic pain, insomnia, headache and backache);

- you can achieve deeper relaxation and calm, particularly with the meditation and self-hypnosis stages of each exercise;

- you will achieve better focus, clarity of mind, concentration and productivity; and ultimately,

- you will have a healthy, positive mind, ready to power forward to embrace all that life has to offer.

I wish you health, happiness and most of all, a blissfully free mind.

"The Future belongs to those who believe in the beauty of their dreams." Eleanor Roosevelt

Tim Patch

Buckinghamshire

Notes

INTRODUCTION

[1] Ferrari A., Somerville A., Baxter A., Norman R., Patten S., Vos T., & Whiteford H. (2013). "Global variation in the prevalence and incidence of major depressive disorder: A systematic review of the epidemiological literature". Psychological Medicine, 43(3), 471-481. doi:10.1017/S0033291712001511

[2] Geneva: World Health Organization; 2017 "Depression and Other Common Mental Disorders: Global Health Estimates";. Licence: CC BY-NC-SA 3.0 IGO

[3] "Depression", Media Centre, World Health Organization http://www.who.int/mediacentre/factsheets/fs369/en/

[4] Horwitz A. V. "How an Age of Anxiety Became an Age of Depression." The Milbank Quarterly 88.1 (2010): 112–138. PMC. Web. 26 June 2017

[5] Simpson H.B., Neri, Y., Lewis-Fernández R., Schneier F., "Anxiety Disorders – Theory, Research and Clinical Perspectives"; Published by Cambridge Medicine ISBN: 9780521515573

[6] NICE: https://www.nice.org.uk/guidance/cg113/chapter/1-guidance.

[7] Mind UK https://www.mind.org.uk

[8] Linda E. Carlson PHD et al. "Mindfulness-Based Cancer Recovery and Supportive-Expressive Therapy Maintain Telomere Length Relative to Controls in Distressed Breast Cancer Survivors" https://onlinelibrary.wiley.com/doi/epdf/10.1002/cncr.29063

[9] Beecher H.K. "THE POWERFUL PLACEBO". JAMA. 1955;159(17):1602–1606. doi:10.1001/jama.1955.02960340022006 https://jamanetwork.com/journals/jama/article-abstract/303530

[10] Moseley B., M.D., O'Malley K, Ph.D., Petersen N.J., Ph.D., Menke T.J., Ph.D., Brody B.A., Ph.D., Kuykendall D.H., Ph.D., Hollingsworth J.C., Dr.P.H., Ashton C.A., M.D., M.P.H., and Wray N., M.D., M.P.H. "A controlled Trial of Arthroscopic Surgery for Osteoarthritis of the Knee". July 11, 2002; N Engl J Med 2002; 347:81-88; DOI: 10.1056/NEJMoa013259; http://www.nejm.org/doi/full/10.1056/NEJMoa013259

MY STORY

[1] Mental Health Statistics, Young Minds UK Charity for mental health and wellbeing in young people; https://youngminds.org.uk/about-us/media-centre/mental-health-stats/

[2] Gashes Kelsang Gyatso "Clear Light of Bliss – Tantric Meditation Manual, Tharpa Publications, 1992; ISBN 0 948006 218

FEAR AND ANXIETY – THE BASICS

[1] Shechner, T., Hong, M., Britton, J., Pine, D., & Fox, N. (2014). "Fear conditioning and extinction across development: Evidence from human studies and animal models". Biological Psychology, 100, 1-12.

[2] Gibson, E. J., & Walk, R. D. (1960). The "visual cliff." Scientific American, 202, 67–71.

WHAT IS ANXIETY?

[1] Reynolds G., Field A.P., and Askew C., "Learning to fear a second-order stimulus following vicarious learning" http://www.tandfonline.com/doi/citedby/10.1080/02699931.2015.1116978?scroll=top&needAccess=true

[2] Gregory A.M., Lau J.Y., and Eley T.C.,. "Finding gene-environment interactions for phobias." European Archives of Psychiatry and Clinical Neuroscience 258.2 (2008): 76-81

[3] Phelps E.A, O'Connor K.J, Gatenby J.C, Grillon C., Gore J.C., Davis M: "Activation of the left amygdala to a cognitive representation of fear" Nat Neurosci2001,4:437-441

HOW ANXIETY IS TRIGGERED BY THE AMYGDALA

[1] Ohman A., Mineka S., "Fears, Phobias, and preparedness: toward an evolved module of fear and fear learning." Psychol Rev. 2001 Jul;108(3):483-522. Review. PubMed PMID: 11488376

HOW ANXIETY IS TRIGGERED BY THE CORTEX

[1] Fuster, Joaquín. "Frontal lobe and cognitive development." Brain Cell Biology 31.5 (2004): 373-385

WHY TRAIN THE MIND?

[1] Lodish H, Berk A, Zipursky SL, et al. Molecular Cell Biology. 4th edition. New York: W. H. Freeman; 2000. Section 21.1, Overview of Neuron Structure and Function. Available from: https://www.ncbi.nlm.nih.gov/books/NBK21535/

[2] James Randerson, 28 February 2012, The Guardian, "How many neurons make a human brain? Billions fewer than we thought." https://www.theguardian.com/science/blog/2012/feb/28/how-many-neurons-human-brain

[3] Herculano-Houzel S. "The Human Brain in Numbers: A Linearly Scaled-up Primate Brain, Frontiers in Human Neuroscience". 2009;3:31.doi:10.3389/neuro.09.031.2009 https://www.ncbi.nlm.nih.gov/pmc/articles/PMC2776484/

[4] Andreasen N. C., (2011), "A Journey into Chaos: Creativity and the Unconscious". In: Brain, Mind and Consciousness: An International, Interdisciplinary Perspective (A.R. Singh and S.A. Singh eds.), MSM, 9(1), p42-53

[5] Woollett K, Maguire EA. "Acquiring the Knowledge of London's Layout Drives Structural Brain Changes". Current Biology. 2011;21(24-2):2109-2114. doi:10.1016/j.cub.2011.11.018. https://www.ncbi.nlm.nih.gov/pmc/articles/PMC3268356/

[6] Erickson K.I., Prakash R.S., Voss M.W., et al. "Aerobic Fitness is Associated With Hippocampal Volume in Elderly Humans". Hippocampus. 2009;19(10):1030-1039. doi:10.1002/hipo.20547. https://www.ncbi.nlm.nih.gov/pmc/articles/PMC3072565/

[7] Luders E., Thompson P.M., Kurth F., Hong J.Y., Phillips O.R., Wang Y., Gutman, B.A., Chou Y.Y., Narr K.L., and Toga A.W., "Global and regional alterations of hippocampal anatomy in long-term meditation practitioners." Human Brain Mapping 34.12 (2013): 3369-3375. https://www.ncbi.nlm.nih.gov/pmc/articles/PMC4084509/

[8] Biegler, Robert et al. "A Larger Hippocampus Is Associated with Longer-Lasting Spatial Memory." Proceedings of the National Academy of Sciences of the United States of America 98.12 (2001): 6941–6944. PMC. Web. 24 Aug. 2017

[9] Nouchi R, Taki Y, Takeuchi H, et al. "Brain Training Game Boosts Executive Functions, Working Memory and Processing Speed in the Young Adults: A Randomized Controlled Trial". Kline AE, ed. PLoS ONE. 2013;8(2):e55518.doi:10.1371/journal.pone.0055518. https://www.ncbi.nlm.nih.gov/pmc/articles/PMC3566110/

[10] Nudo R.J. "Recovery after brain injury: mechanisms and principles". Frontiers in Human Neuroscience. 2013;7:887. doi:10.3389/fnhum.2013.00887. https://www.ncbi.nlm.nih.gov/pmc/articles/PMC3870954/

THE CONSCIOUS MIND

[1] Heyes C., "New thinking: the evolution of human cognition." Philosophical Transactions of the Royal Society B: Biological Sciences. 2012;367(1599):2091-2096.doi:10.1098/rstb.2012.0111. https://www.ncbi.nlm.nih.gov/pmc/articles/PMC3385676/

[2] Masicampo E.J, Baumeister R.F., "Conscious thought does not guide moment-to-moment actions—it serves social and cultural functions." Frontiers in Psychology. 2013;4:478. doi:10.3389/fpsyg.2013.00478

[3] Pagnoni G., Cekic M., & Guo Y. (2008). "Thinking about Not-Thinking": Neural Correlates of Conceptual Processing during Zen Meditation. PLoS ONE, 3(9).

[4] Alexandra Richards, Evening Standard, World News, July 10 2018. "Thailand cave rescue news: Meditation led by coach helped boys survive terrifying ordeal, family say " https://www.standard.co.uk/news/world/thailand-cave-rescue-meditation-led-by-coach-helped-boys-survive-terrifying-ordeal-family-say-a3883386.html

[5] Adrienne A. Taren, P.C.E.A.K.R.J.E.A.J.J.J. (2015). "Mindfulness meditation training alters stress-related amygdala resting state functional connectivity: a randomized controlled trial." Social Cognitive and Affective Neuroscience, 10(12)

[6] Massachussets General Hospital, News Release, January 2011; "Mindfulness Meditation training changes brain structure in 8 weeks" http://www.massgeneral.org/about/pressrelease.aspx?id=1329

[7] Berkely News, University of California, Berkely News, February 2014; "New evidence that chronic stress predisposes brain to mental illness" http://news.berkeley.edu/2014/02/11/chronic-stress-predisposes-brain-to-mental-illness/

[8] Medford, N., & Critchley, H. (2010). "Conjoint activity of anterior insular and anterior cingulate cortex: awareness and response". Brain Structure and Function, 214(6), 535-549.

[9] Luders E., Phillips O.R., Clark K., Kurth F., Toga A.W., Narr K.L., "Bridging the Hemispheres in Meditation: thicker callosal regions and enhanced fractional anisotropy (FA) in long-term practitioners". Neuroimage. 2012;61(1):181-187. doi:10.1016/j.neuroimage.2012.02.026.

[10] Luders E., Narr K.L., Bilder R.M., et al. "Positive Correlations between Corpus Callosum Thickness and Intelligence". NeuroImage. 2007;37(4):1457-1464. doi:10.1016/j.neuroimage.2007.06.028.

[11] Hölzel B. K., Carmody J., Vangel M., Congleton C., Yerramsetti S. M., Gard T., & Lazar S. W. (2011). "Mindfulness practice leads to increases in regional brain gray matter density". Psychiatry Research, 191(1), 36–43. http://doi.org/10.1016/j.pscychresns.2010.08.006

[12] UCLA Newsroom, July 2008, "Practice of mindfulness meditation slows the progression of HIV, study shows." UCLA newsroom, http://newsroom.ucla.edu/releases/mindfulness-meditation-slows-progression-53819

[13] Linda E. Carlson PHD et al. "Mindfulness-Based Cancer Recovery and Supportive-Expressive Therapy Maintain Telomere Length Relative to Controls in Distressed Breast Cancer Survivors" https://onlinelibrary.wiley.com/doi/epdf/10.1002/cncr.29063

THE SUBCONSCIOUS MIND

[1] Perlovsky L., Ilin R., "Brain. Conscious and unconscious mechanisms of cognition, emotions, and language"; https://www.ncbi.nlm.nih.gov/pubmed/24961270

[2] Bargh J.A., Chen M., Burrows L., "Automaticity of Social Behavior: Direct Effects of Trait Construct and Stereotype Activation on Action" https://www.psychologytoday.com/files/attachments/5089/barghch enburrows1996.pdf

[3] Brunner, T. A. "How weight-related cues affect food intake in a modelling situation." Appetite 55.3 (2010): 507-511.

[4] Jean-Charles Chebat, Richard Michon, "impact of ambient odors on mall shoppers' emotions, cognition and spending – a test of competitive arousal theories"; Journal of Business Research, 56(2003) 529-539 http://www.ryerson.ca/~rmichon/Publications/Ambient%20odors.pd f

[5] Jones B.C., DeBruine L.M., Little A.C., Burriss R.P., Feinberg D.R.

Proc. R. Soc. B 2007 274 899-903; DOI: 10.1098/rspb.2006.0205. Published 22 March 2007 http://rspb.royalsocietypublishing.org/content/274/1611/899.full?si d=7ab743a6-f355-4bd5-bb97-d7246ebaa864

[6] Functional magnetic resonance imaging or functional MRI (fMRI) measures brain activity by detecting changes associated with blood flow. This technique relies on the fact that cerebral blood flow and neuronal activation are coupled.

[7] Unconscious decisions in the brain." Max-Planck-Gesellschaft https://www.mpg.de/research/unconscious-decisions-in-the-brain

[8] Electroencephalogram (EEG) is a test that detects electrical activity in your brain using small, flat metal discs (electrodes) attached to your scalp. Your brain cells communicate via electrical impulses and are active all the time, even when you're asleep. This activity shows up as wavy lines on an EEG recording.

[9] Saxby E., Peniston E.G., "Alpha-theta brainwave neurofeedback training: an effective treatment for male and female alcoholics with depressive symptoms". J Clin Psychol. 1995 Sep;51(5):685-93. PubMed PMID: 8801245
https://www.ncbi.nlm.nih.gov/pubmed/8801245?dopt=Abstract

[10] Jensen, Mark P. et al. "MECHANISMS OF HYPNOSIS:: Toward the Development of a Biopsychosocial Model." The International journal of clinical and experimental hypnosis 63.1 (2015): 34–75. PMC. Web. 8 May 2018.
https://www.ncbi.nlm.nih.gov/pmc/articles/PMC4220267/#R72

[11] Ulrike H., "Learning and Recall Under Hypnosis"; Reference work entry; Encyclopedia of the Sciences of Learning; pp 1793-1797; https://link.springer.com/referenceworkentry/10.1007%2F978-1-4419-1428-6_168

[12] About Milton Erickson, cited with permission from Ericksonian.com: http://ericksonian.com/about/milton-erickson

[13] Milton Erickson, Wikepedia.org:
https://en.wikipedia.org/wiki/Milton_H._Erickson

[14] On Esdaile and hypnotic anaesthetic" The UK College of Hypnosis and Hypnotherapy
https://www.ukhypnosis.com/2011/03/02/on-esdaile-and-hypnotic-anaesthetic-from-the-complete-writings-of-james-braid/

[15]Robert S. Bobrow, M.D. "The Witch in the Waiting Room: A physician investigates paranormal phenomena." Published by Thunder's Mouth Press ISBN-13: 978-1560258148

[16] Tachistoscope: an instrument used for exposing objects to the eye for a very brief measured period of time.

[17] Siemionow V., Liu J.Z., Sahgal V., and Yue G.H., "From Mental Power to Muscle Power" – Gaining Strength By Using the Mind" by Ranganathan VK, https://www.ncbi.nlm.nih.gov/pubmed/14998709

[18] Pascual-Leone A., Amedi A., Fregni F., and Merabet L.B.; Center for Non-Invasive Brain Stimulation, Department of Neurology, Beth Israel Deaconess Medical Center; Harvard Medical School, Boston, Massachusetts 02215; "The Plastic Human Brain Cortex" http://brain.huji.ac.il/publications/Pascual-Leone_Amedi_et%20al%20Ann%20Rev%20Neurosci%2005.pdf

[19] Liggett D.R., Ph.D. and Hamada S., "Enhancing the Visualization of Gymnasts"; American Journal of Clinical Hypnosis Vol. 35 , Iss. 3,1993 http://www.tandfonline.com/action/showCitFormats?doi=10.1080%2F00029157.1993.10403003

THE TRAINING PROGRAMME:

OVERCOMING SELF-CONSCIOUSNESS AND ERADICATING PRE-JUDGEMENT

[1] Laufer O., Israeli D., Paz R., "Behavioral and Neural Mechanisms of Overgeneralization in Anxiety"; Curr Biol. 2016 Mar 21;26(6):713-22. doi: 10.1016/j.cub.2016.01.023. Epub 2016 Mar 3.

[2] The Office for National Statistics, Statitical Bulletin. "Divorces in England and Wales, 2016" https://www.ons.gov.uk/peoplepopulationandcommunity/birthsdeathsandmarriages/divorce/bulletins/divorcesinenglandandwales/2016

LETTING GO OF CONTROL

[1] Lachman, M. E., & Weaver, S. L. (1998). "The sense of control as a moderator of social class differences in health and well-being". Journal of Personality and Social Psychology, 74(3), 763-773. http://dx.doi.org/10.1037/0022-3514.74.3.763

CHALLENGING A FEAR OF FAILURE

[1] Andrew M.J., and Marsh H.W., "Fear of Failure: Friend or Foe?" Australian Psychologist 38.1 (2003

[2] Michael Schuman, Japan Times Bloomberg, November 2016; "Japan may be too scared of failure to succeed." http://www.japantimes.co.jp/opinion/2016/11/01/commentary/japan-commentary/japan-may-scared-failure-succeed/#.WV-vYFGQy1s

[3] Paul R. La Monica, CNN Money Online, February 2018 "Apple is leading the race to $1 trillion" http://money.cnn.com/2018/02/27/investing/apple-google-amazon-microsoft-trillion-dollar-market-value/index.html

[4] Zoe Wood, The Guardian, February 2014; "Facebook turned down WhatsApp co-founder for a job in 2009" https://www.theguardian.com/technology/2014/feb/20/facebook-turned-down-whatsapp-co-founder-brian-acton-job-2009

[5] Dominic Rush, The Guardian, February 2014; "WhatsApp: Facebook acquires messaging service in $19bn deal" https://www.theguardian.com/technology/2014/feb/19/facebook-buys-whatsapp-16bn-deal

[6] Paul, R. La Monica, CNN Money Online, February 2018; "Apple is leading the race to $1 trillion" http://money.cnn.com/2018/02/27/investing/apple-google-amazon-microsoft-trillion-dollar-market-value/index.html

[7] Maev Kennedy, The Guardian, March 2016; "JK Rowling posts letters of rejection on Twitter to help budding authors" https://www.theguardian.com/books/2016/mar/25/jk-rowling-harry-potter-posts-letters-of-rejection-on-twitter

[8] "Crashing an Airliner on Purpose. Stunt or Science?" Royal Aeronautical Society https://www.aerosociety.com/news/crashing-an-airliner-on-purpose-stunt-or-science/

CHALLENGING A FEAR OF SUCCESS

[1] Napoleon Hill, "Think and Grow Rich", ISBN: 978-0990797609

LIVE AND WORK IN THE ZONE

[1] Helmenstine A.M., Ph.D Thought & Co; "How many atoms in the human body?" https://www.thoughtco.com/how-many-atoms-are-in-human-body-603872

[2] Bianconi et al, 2013; National Institutes of Health; "An estimation of the number of cells in the human body." https://www.ncbi.nlm.nih.gov/pubmed/23829164

[3] Carlson L. E., Beattie T. L., Giese-Davis J., Faris P., Tamagawa R., Fick L. J., Degelman E. S. and Speca M. (2015); "Mindfulness-based cancer recovery and supportive-expressive therapy maintain telomere length relative to controls in distressed breast cancer survivors". Cancer, 121: 476–484. doi:10.1002/cncr.29063 http://onlinelibrary.wiley.com/doi/10.1002/cncr.29063/full

[4] Adam Hadhazy, Scientific American, February 2010; "Think Twice: How the Gut's Second Brain Influences Mood and Wellbeing", Scientific American https://www.scientificamerican.com/article/gut-second-brain/

[5] Justin Sonnenburg and Erica Sonnenburg, Scientific American, May 2015; "Gut Feelings: The Second Brain in our Gastrointestinal System" https://www.scientificamerican.com/article/gut-feelings-the-second-brain-in-our-gastrointestinal-systems-excerpt/

[6] "Blueberries: antioxidant powerhouse?" NHS Choices online https://www.nhs.uk/live-well/eat-well/are-blueberries-a-superfood/

[7] Smith et al, 2010; "Homocysteine-lowering by B vitamins slows the rate of accelerated brain atrophy in mild cognitive impairment: a randomized controlled trial." https://www.ncbi.nlm.nih.gov/pubmed/20838622

[8] Giacopo et al, 2015; "An overview on neuroprotective effects of isothiocyanates for the treatment of neurodegenerative diseases". https://www.ncbi.nlm.nih.gov/pubmed/26254971

[9] The Harvard Mahoney Neuroscience Institute Letter; "Sugar and the brain"; http://neuro.hms.harvard.edu/harvard-mahoney-neuroscience-institute/brain-newsletter/and-brain-series/sugar-and-brain

[10] The Harvard Mahoney Neuroscience Institute Letter; "Sugar and the brain"; http://neuro.hms.harvard.edu/harvard-mahoney-neuroscience-institute/brain-newsletter/and-brain-series/sugar-and-brain

[11] Bertram L., & Heekeren, H. (2010). "Obesity and the brain: a possible genetic link". Alzheimer's Research & Therapy, 2, 27-27

[12] O'Neil et al, 2014; "Relationship Between Diet and Mental Health in Children and Adolescents: A Systematic Review". https://www.ncbi.nlm.nih.gov/pmc/articles/PMC4167107/

[13] "Walking and Health" BUPA Healthcare https://www.bupa.co.uk/health-information/directory/w/walking-health

[14] The MOVES App http://www.moves-app.com/

WHAT NEXT?

[1] Guest, P.C., Springer International AG, 2017; "Biomarkers and Mental Illness – It's Not All In The Mind." ISBN 978-3-319-46087-1

[2] Norton, P. J. "A Randomized Clinical Trial of Transdiagnostic CBT for Anxiety Disorder by Comparison to Relaxation Training." Behavior therapy 43.3 (2012): 506–517. PMC. Web. 4 June 2018. https://www.ncbi.nlm.nih.gov/pmc/articles/PMC3484173/

[3] According to Mind mental health charity the UK, the 9 common anxiety disorders are: Generalised Anxiety Disorder (GAD); Social Anxiety Disorder; Panic Disorder; Phobias; Post Traumatic Stress Disorder (PSTD); Obsessive Compulsive Disorder (OCD); Body dysmorphic disorder (BDD); Perinatal anxiety or perinatal OCD. https://www.mind.org.uk for further information

[4] Barlow D.H., "Unified Protocol for Transdiagnostic Treatment of Emotional Disorders: Workbook (Treatments That Work)"; ASIN: B00I613KIO; Published by OUP USA, (2011).

Printed in Great Britain
by Amazon

40110287R00108